Penguin
The Com

With an essay by
MICHEL DE MONTAIGNE

PENGUIN BOOKS

PENGUIN CLASSICS

Published by the Penguin Group
Penguin Books Ltd, 80 Strand, London WC2R ORL, England
Penguin Group (USA) Inc., 375 Hudson Street, New York, New York 10014, USA
Penguin Group (Canada), 90 Eglinton Avenue East, Suite 700, Toronto, Ontario, Canada M4P 2Y3
(a division of Pearson Penguin Canada Inc.)
Penguin Ireland, 25 St Stephen's Green, Dublin 2, Ireland (a division of Penguin Books Ltd)
Penguin Group (Australia), 707 Collins Street,
Melbourne, Victoria 3008, Australia (a division of Pearson Australia Group Pty Ltd)
Penguin Books India Pvt Ltd, 11 Community Centre, Panchsheel Park,
New Delhi – 110 017, India
Penguin Group (NZ), 67 Apollo Drive, Rosedale, Auckland 0632, New Zealand
(a division of Pearson New Zealand Ltd)
Penguin Books (South Africa) (Pty) Ltd, Block D, Rosebank Office Park, 181 Jan Smuts Avenue,
Parktown North, Gauteng 2193, South Africa

Penguin Books Ltd, Registered Offices: 80 Strand, London WC2R ORL, England

www.penguin.com

'On Books' by Michel de Montaigne first published in this translation,
in *The Complete Essays*, by Penguin Classics 1991
Penguin Classics: The Complete List first published by Penguin Classics 2013
001

Translation of 'On Books' copyright © M. A. Screech, 1991
All rights reserved

The moral right of the translator has been asserted

Set in 10.25/13.25pt PostScript Adobe Sabon
Typeset by Dinah Drazin
Printed in Great Britain by Clays Ltd, St Ives plc

ISBN: 978-0-141-38941-7

www.greenpenguin.co.uk

ALWAYS LEARNING   **PEARSON**

Contents

Also available:

Penguin Modern Classics: The Complete List
9780141197401

A–Z BY AUTHOR

A

* = forthcoming title after March 2013

ABBOTT, EDWIN A. *Flatland*
Introduced by Alan Lightman
9780140435313

ABELARD, PETER *The Letters of Abelard and Heloise*
Translated and edited by M. T. Clanchy and Betty
Radice
9780140448993

ADOMNÁN OF IONA *Life of St Columba*
Translated by Richard Sharpe
9780140444629

AESCHYLUS *Prometheus Bound and Other Plays*
Translated and edited by Philip Vellacott
9780140441123
The Oresteia
Translated by Robert Fagles
9780140443332
The Oresteian Trilogy
Translated by Philip Vellacott
9780140440676

The Persians and Other Plays
    Translated and edited by Alan H. Sommerstein
    9780140449990

AESCHYLUS, SOPHOCLES, EURIPIDES, ARISTOPHANES
    AND ARISTOTLE *Greek Tragedy*
    Edited by Shomit Dutta and introduced by Simon
    Goldhill (various translators)
    9780141439365

AESOP *The Complete Fables*
    Translated and edited by Olivia and Robert Temple
    9780140446494

African Myths of Origin
    Edited by Stephen Belcher
    9780140449457

AKUTAGAWA, RYUNOSUKE *Rashōmon and Seventeen Other
    Stories*
    Translated and edited by Jay Rubin and introduced by
    Haruki Murakami
    9780140449709

ALAIN-FOURNIER, HENRI *The Lost Estate (Le Grand
    Meaulnes)*
    Translated by Robin Buss and introduced by Adam
    Gopnik
    9780141441894

ALAS, LEOPOLDO *La Regenta*
    Translated by John Rutherford
    9780140443462

ALBERTI, LEON BATTISTA *On Painting*
    Translated by Cecil Grayson and introduced by Martin
    Kemp
    9780140433319

ALCOTT, LOUISA MAY *Little Women*
Introduced by Elaine Showalter
9780140390698

ALDINGTON, RICHARD *Death of a Hero* *
Introduced by James H. Meredith
9780143106876

ALEICHEM, SHOLEM *Tevye the Dairyman* and *Motl the Cantor's Son*
Translated by Aliza Shevrin and introduced by Dan Miron
9780143105602

ALIGHIERI, DANTE *Dante in English*
Edited by Eric Griffiths and Matthew Reynolds (various translators)
9780140423884
Inferno
Translated by Robin Kirkpatrick
9780140448955
Paradiso
Translated by Robin Kirkpatrick
9780140448979
Purgatorio
Translated by Robin Kirkpatrick
9780140448962
The Divine Comedy I: Hell
Translated by Dorothy L. Sayers
9780140440065
The Divine Comedy II: Purgatory
Translated by Dorothy L. Sayers
9780140440461
The Divine Comedy III: Paradise
Translated by Dorothy L. Sayers and introduced by Barbara Reynolds
9780140441055

The Divine Comedy (Volume I): Inferno
Translated by Mark Musa
9780142437223
The Divine Comedy (Volume II): Purgatory
Translated by Mark Musa
978014044421
The Divine Comedy (Volume III): Paradise
Translated by Mark Musa
9780140444438
The Divine Comedy: Inferno, Purgatorio, Paradiso
Translated by Robin Kirkpatrick
9780141197494
Vita Nuova
Translated by Barbara Reynolds
9780140449471

ALLEN, GRANT *An African Millionaire*
Introduced by Gary Hoppenstand
9780143106579

AMADO, JORGE *Captains of the Sands* *
Translated by Gregory Rabassa and introduced by Colm
    Tóibín
9780143106357
The Discovery of America by the Turks
Translated by Gregory Rabassa
9780143106982
The Double Death of Quincas Water-Bray
Translated by Gregory Rabassa
9780143106364
The Violent Land *
Translated by Samuel Putnam and introduced by Alfred
    MacAdam
9780143106371

APULEIUS *The Golden Ass*
Translated by E. J. Kenney
9780140435900

AQUINAS, SAINT THOMAS *Selected Writings*
Translated and edited by Ralph McInerny
9780140436327

The Arabian Nights: Tales of 1,001 Nights (Volume I)
Translated by Malcolm C. Lyons with Ursula Lyons and
introduced by Robert Irwin
9780140449389

The Arabian Nights: Tales of 1,001 Nights (Volume II)
Translated by Malcolm C. Lyons with Ursula Lyons and
introduced by Robert Irwin
9780140449396

The Arabian Nights: Tales of 1,001 Nights (Volume III)
Translated by Malcolm C. Lyons with Ursula Lyons and
introduced by Robert Irwin
9780140449402

ARENDT, HANNAH *Eichmann in Jerusalem: A Report on the
Banality of Evil*
Introduced by Amos Elon
9780143039884
On Revolution
9780143039907
The Portable Hannah Arendt
Introduced by Peter Baehr
9780142437568

ARIOSTO, LUDOVICO *Orlando Furioso Part I*
Translated by Barbara Reynolds
9780140443110
Orlando Furioso Part II
Translated by Barbara Reynolds
9780140443103

The Metaphysics
Translated by Hugh Lawson-Tancred
9780140446197
The Nicomachean Ethics
Translated by J. A. K. Thomson, revised by Hugh
   Tredennick and introduced by Jonathan Barnes
9780140449495
The Politics
Translated by T. A. Sinclair, revised by Trevor J.
   Saunders
9780140444216

ARRIAN *The Campaigns of Alexander*
Translated by Aubrey de Sélincourt, revised by
   J. R. Hamilton
9780140442533

ASSER ET AL. *Alfred the Great: Asser's Life of King Alfred
   and Other Contemporary Sources*
Translated and edited by Simon Keynes and Michael
   Lapidge
9780140444094

ATTAR, FARID UD-DIN *The Conference of the Birds*
Translated by Afkham Darbandi and Dick Davis
9780140444346

AUGUSTINE, SAINT *City of God*
Translated by Henry Bettenson and introduced by
   G. R. Evans
9780140448948
Confessions
Translated by R. S. Pine-Coffin
9780140441147

B

BABEL, ISAAC *Red Cavalry and Other Stories*
Translated and edited by Efraim Sicher and introduced
by David McDuff
9780140449976

BACON, FRANCIS *The Essays*
Edited by John Pitcher
9780140432169

BALZAC, HONORÉ DE *A Harlot High and Low*
Translated by Rayner Heppenstall
9780140442328
Cousin Bette
Translated by Marion Ayton Crawford
9780140441604
Cousin Pons
Translated by Herbert J. Hunt
9780140442052
Eugénie Grandet
Translated by M. A. Crawford
9780140440508
History of the Thirteen
Translated by Herbert J. Hunt
9780140443011

BAUDELAIRE, CHARLES-PIERRE *Selected Poems*
Translated and edited by Carol Clark
9780140446241
Selected Writings on Art and Literature
Translated and edited by P. E. Charvet
9780140446067

BAZAN, EMILIA PARDO *The House of Ulloa* *
Translated by Lucia Graves and Paul O'Prey
9780141392950

BEAUMARCHAIS, PIERRE-AUGUSTIN CARON DE
The Barber of Seville and *The Marriage of Figaro*
Translated by John Wood
9780140441338

BECKFORD, WILLIAM *Vathek and Other Stories*
Edited by Malcolm Jack
9780140435306

BECKFORD, WILLIAM, SHELLEY, MARY AND WALPOLE,
HORACE *Three Gothic Novels*
Introduced by Mario Praz
9780140430363

BEDE, T. V., *Ecclesiastical History of the English People*
Translated by Leo Sherley-Price and introduced by
D. H. Farmer
9780140445657

BEDE, T. V., ET AL. *The Age of Bede*
Translated and edited by D. H. Farmer and J. F. Webb
9780140447279

BEHN, APHRA *Oroonoko*
Edited by Janet Todd
9780140439885

BÉROUL *The Romance of Tristan*
Translated by Alan S. Fedrick
9780140442304

The Bhagavad Gita
Translated by Laurie L. Patton
9780140447903

The Bible
Edited by David Norton
9780141441511

BLACKMORE, RICHARD DODDRIDGE *Lorna Doone*
Edited by Michelle Allen and R. D. Madison
9780143039327

BLAKE, WILLIAM *Selected Poems*
Edited by G. E. Bentley Jnr
9780140424461
The Complete Poems
Edited by Alicia Ostriker
9780140422153

BLIGH, WILLIAM AND CHRISTIAN, EDWARD *The Bounty
Mutiny*
Edited by R. D. Madison
9780140439168

BOCCACCIO, GIOVANNI *The Decameron*
Translated by G. H. McWilliam
9780140449303

BOETHIUS *The Consolation of Philosophy*
Translated by Victor Watts
9780140447804

The Book of Common Prayer
Introduced by James Wood
9780143106562

The Book of Dede Korkut
  Translated by Geoffrey Lewis
  9780141199030

BOOTHBY, GUY *Prince of Swindlers* *
  Introduced by Gary Hoppenstand
  9780143107224

BOROWSKI, TADEUSZ *This Way for the Gas, Ladies and
    Gentlemen*
  Translated by Barbara Vedder and introduced by
    Jan Kott
  9780140186246

BOSWELL, JAMES *Boswell's London Journal 1762–1763*
  Edited by Gordon Turnbull
  9780140436501
  The Life of Samuel Johnson
  Edited by David Womersley
  9780140436624

BOSWELL, JAMES AND JOHNSON, SAMUEL *A Journey to the
    Western Islands of Scotland* and *The Journal of a Tour
    to the Hebrides*
  Edited by Peter Levi
  9780140432213

BRADDON, MARY ELIZABETH *Lady Audley's Secret*
  Edited by Jenny Bourne Taylor
  9780140435849

BRADLEY, A. C. *Shakespearean Tragedy*
  Introduced by John Bayley
  9780140530193

BRILLAT-SAVARIN, JEAN-ANTHELME *The Physiology of
    Taste*
  Translated by Anne Drayton
  9780140446142

BRONTË, ANNE *Agnes Grey*
Edited by Angeline Goreau
9780140432107
The Tenant of Wildfell Hall
Edited by Stevie Davis
9780140434743

BRONTË, CHARLOTTE *Jane Eyre*
Edited by Stevie Davis
9780141441146
Shirley
Edited by Jessica Cox and introduced by Lucasta Miller
9780141439860
Tales of Angria
Edited by Heather Glen
9780140435092
The Professor
Edited by Heather Glen
9780140433111
Villette
Edited by Helen Cooper
9780140434798

BRONTË, EMILY *The Complete Poems*
Edited by Janet Gezari
9780140423525
Wuthering Heights
Edited by Pauline Nestor and introduced by Lucasta
Miller
9780141439556

BROWNE, SIR THOMAS *The Major Works*
Edited by C. A. Patrides
9780140431094

BROWNING, ELIZABETH BARRETT *Aurora Leigh and Other Poems*
Edited by John Robert Glorney Bolton and Julia Bolton Holloway
9780140434125

BROWNING, ROBERT *Selected Poems*
Edited by Daniel Karlin
9780140437263

BUCHAN, JOHN *The Strange Adventures of Mr Andrew Hawthorn and Other Stories*
Edited by John Keegan and introduced by Giles Foden
9780141442426
The Thirty-Nine Steps
Edited by John Keegan
9780141441177

BÜCHNER, GEORG *Complete Plays, Lenz and Other Writings*
Translated and edited by John Reddick
9780140445862

Buddhist Scriptures
Translated and edited by Donald S. Lopez Jnr
9780140447583

BULGAKOV, MIKHAIL *A Dead Man's Memoir*
Translated by Andrew Bromfield and introduced by Keith Gessen
9780140455144
A Dog's Heart
Translated by Andrew Bromfield and introduced by James Meek
9780140455151
The Master and Margarita
Translated by Richard Pevear and Larissa Volokhonsky
9780140455465

BUNIN, IVAN *The Gentleman from San Francisco and Other
          Stories*
     Translated and edited by David Richards
     9780140185522

BUNYAN, JOHN *Grace Abounding to the Chief of Sinners*
     Edited by W. R. Owens
     9780140432800
   The Pilgrim's Progress
     Edited by Roger Pooley
     9780141439716

BURCKHARDT, JACOB *The Civilization of the Renaissance in
          Italy*
     Translated by S. G. C. Middlemore and introduced by
          Peter Burke
     9780140445343

BURKE, EDMUND *A Philosophical Enquiry into the Sublime
          and Beautiful*
     Edited by David Womersley
     9780140436259
   Reflections on the Revolution in France
     Edited by Conor Cruise O'Brien
     9780140432046

BURNETT, FRANCES HODGSON *A Little Princess*
     Edited by U. C. Knoepflmacher
   The Secret Garden
     Edited by Alison Lurie
     9780142437056

BURNEY, FRANCES *Evelina*
     Edited by Margaret Anne Doody
     9780140433470
   Journals and Letters
     Edited by Peter Sabor and Lars E. Troide
     9780140436242

BURNS, ROBERT *Poems of Robert Burns*
Edited by Carol McGuirk
9780140423822

BUTLER, SAMUEL *Erewhon: or, Over the Range*
Edited by Peter Mudford
9780140430578
The Way of All Flesh
Edited by James Cochrane and introduced by Richard
Hoggart
9780140430127

BYRON, LORD *Don Juan*
Edited by W. W. Pratt, E. Steffan and T. G. Steffan and
introduced by Peter J. Manning and Susan J. Wolfson
9780140424522
Selected Poems
Edited by Peter J. Manning and Susan J. Wolfson
9780140424508

BYRON, ROBERT *The Road to Oxiana*
Introduced by Colin Thubron
9780141442099

C

CASSIUS DIO *The Roman History*
Translated by Ian Scott-Kilvert and introduced by John
    Carter
9780140444483

CASTIGLIONE, BALDESSARE *The Book of the Courtier*
Translated by George Bull
9780140441925

CATLIN, GEORGE *North American Indians*
Edited by Peter Matthiessen
9780142437506

CATULLUS *The Poems*
Translated by Peter Wigham
9780140449815

CAVAFY, CONSTANTINE P. *The Selected Poems of Cavafy*
Translated and edited by Avi Sharon
9780141185613

CAVENDISH, MARGARET *The Blazing World and Other*
    Writings
Edited by Kate Lilley
9780140433722

CELLINI, BENVENUTO *Autobiography*
Translated by George Bull
9780140447187

A Celtic Miscellany
Edited by Kenneth Hurlstone Jackson
9780140442472

CERVANTES, MIGUEL DE *Don Quixote*
Translated by John Rutherford
9780140449099
Exemplary Stories
Translated by C. A. Jones
9780140442489

CHEKHOV, ANTON *A Life in Letters*
Translated and edited by Rosamund Bartlett and
   Anthony Phillips
9780140449228
Plays
Translated by Peter Carson, edited by Ronald Wilkes and
   introduced by Richard Gilman
9780140447330
The Lady with the Little Dog and Other Stories,
   1896–1904
Translated and edited by Ronald Wilks and introduced
   by Paul Debreczeny
9780140447873
The Shooting Party
Translated by Ronald Wilks and introduced by John
   Sutherland
9780140448986
The Steppe and Other Stories, 1887–91
Translated and edited by Ronald Wilks and introduced
   by Ronald Wayfield
9780140447859
Ward No. 6 and Other Stories, 1892–1895
Translated and edited by Ronald Wilks and introduced
   by J. Douglas Clayton
9780140447866

CHESNUT, MARY BOYKIN *Mary Chesnut's Diary*
Introduced by Catherine Clinton
9780143106067

CHESTERTON, G. K. *The Complete Father Brown Stories*
Edited by Michael D. Hurley
9780141193854
The Man Who Was Thursday
Edited by Matthew Beaumont
9780141191461

The Second World War (Volume IV): The Hinge of Fate
Introduced by John Keegan
9780141441757
The Second World War (Volume V): Closing the Ring
Introduced by John Keegan
9780141441764
The Second World War (Volume VI): Triumph and Tragedy
Introduced by John Keegan
9780141441771
The World Crisis 1911–1918
Introduced by Martin Gilbert
9780141442051

CICERO *In Defence of the Republic*
Translated by Siobhan McElduff
9780140455533
Murder Trials
Translated and edited by Michael Grant
9780140442885
On Government
Translated by Michael Grant
9780140445954
On Living and Dying Well
Translated by Thomas Habinek
9780140455564
On the Good Life
Translated by Michael Grant
9780140442441
Selected Letters
Translated and edited by D. R. Shackleton Bailey
9780140444582
Selected Political Speeches
Translated and edited by Michael Grant
9780140442144

Selected Works
   Translated and edited by Michael Grant
   9780140440997
The Nature of the Gods
   Translated by Horace C. P. McGregor and introduced by
      J. M. Ross
   9780140442656

*The Cistercian World: Monastic Writings of the Twelfth
      Century*
   Translated and edited by Pauline Matarasso
   9780140433562

CLARE, JOHN *Selected Poems*
   Edited by Geoffrey Summerfield
   9780140437249

Classical Literary Criticism
   Translated and edited by T. S. Dorsch and Penelope
      Murray
   9780140446517

CLAUSEWITZ, CARL VON *On War*
   Translated by Colonel J. J. Graham, revised by Colonel
      F. N. Maude and edited by Anatol Rapoport
   9780140444278

CLELAND, JOHN *Fanny Hill: or, Memoirs of a Woman of
      Pleasure*
   Edited by Peter Wagner
   9780140432497

The Cloud of Unknowing and Other Works
   Translated and edited by A. C. Spearing
   9780140447620

COBB, HUMPHREY *Paths of Glory*
   Introduced by James H. Meredith and David Simon
   9780143106111

COBBETT, WILLIAM *Rural Rides*
Edited by Ian Dyck
9780140435795

COLERIDGE, SAMUEL TAYLOR *Selected Poetry*
Edited by Richard Holmes
9780140424294
The Complete Poems
Edited by William Keach
9780140423532

COLERIDGE, SAMUEL TAYLOR AND WORDSWORTH,
WILLIAM *Lyrical Ballads*
Edited by Michael Schmidt
9780140424621

COLLINS, WILKIE *Armadale*
Edited by John Sutherland
9780140434118
No Name
Edited by Mark Ford
9780140433975
The Law and the Lady
Edited by David Skilton
9780140436075
The Moonstone
Edited by Sandra Kemp
9780140434088
The Woman in White
Edited by Matthew Sweet
9780141439617

COLLODI, CARLO *Pinocchio*
Translated by M. A. Murray, revised by G. Tassinari and
introduced by Jack Zipes
9780142437063

COLUMBUS, CHRISTOPHER *The Four Voyages of
Christopher Columbus*
Translated and edited by J. M. Cohen
9780140442175

Comic Sagas and Tales from Iceland
Edited by Viðar Hreinsson (various translators)
9780140447743

The Complete Dead Sea Scrolls in English
Translated by Geza Vermes
9780141197319

*Con Men and Cutpurses: Scenes from the Hogarthian
Underworld*
Edited by Lucy Moore
9780140437607

CONFUCIUS *The Analects*
Translated by D. C. Lau
9780140443486

CONGREVE, WILLIAM *The Way of the World and Other
Plays*
Edited by Eric S. Rump
9780141441856

CONGREVE, WILLIAM, ETHERIDGE, GEORGE AND
WYCHERLEY, WILLIAM *Three Restoration Comedies*
Edited by Gāmini Salgādo
9780140430271

CONRAD, JOSEPH *Heart of Darkness*
Edited by Owen Knowles
9780141441672
Lord Jim
Edited by Allan H. Simmons
9780141441610

Nostromo
    Edited by Véronique Pauly
    9780141441634
The Nigger of the 'Narcissus' and Other Stories
    Edited by Allan H. Simmons and introduced by Gail
        Fraser
    9780141441702
The Secret Agent
    Edited by Michael Newton
    9780141441580
Typhoon and Other Stories
    Edited by J. H. Stape
    9780141441955
Under Western Eyes
    Edited by Stephen Donovan and introduced by Allan H.
        Simmons
    9780141441948

CONSTANT, HENRI-BENJAMIN *Adolphe*
    Translated by Leonard Tancock
    9780140441345

COOK, CAPTAIN JAMES *Journals*
    Edited by Philip Edwards
    9780140436471

COOPER, JAMES FENIMORE *The Last of the Mohicans*
    Introduced by Richard Slotkin
    9780140390247
The Pioneers
    Introduced by Donald A. Ringe
    9780140390070

CORNEILLE, PIERRE *The Cid, The Cinna, The Theatrical
        Illusion*
    Translated by John Cairncross
    9780140443127

CORNEILLE, PIERRE, MOLIÈRE AND RACINE, JEAN *Four French Plays: Cinna, The Misanthrope, Andromache, Phaedra* *
Translated by John Edmunds and introduced by Joseph Harris
9780141392080

CRANE, STEPHEN *Maggie: A Girl of the Streets and Other Tales of New York*
Edited by Larzer Ziff
9780140437973
The Red Badge of Courage and Other Stories
Edited by Gary Scharnhorst
9780143039358

The Cynic Philosophers: From Diogenes to Julian
Translated and edited by Robert Dobbin
9780141192222

D

The Death of King Arthur
   Translated by James Cable
   9780140442557

The Death of King Arthur: The Immortal Legend
   Retold by Peter Ackroyd
   9780140455656

Decadent Poetry from Wilde to Naidu
   Edited by Lisa Rodensky
   9780140424133

DEFOE, DANIEL *A Journal of the Plague Year*
   Edited by Cynthia Wall
   9780140437850
   A Tour Through the Whole Island of Great Britain
      (Abridged)
   Edited by Pat Rogers
   9780140430660
   Moll Flanders
   Edited by David Blewett
   9780140433135
   Robinson Crusoe
   Edited by John Richetti
   9780141439822
   Roxana
   Edited by David Blewett
   9780140431490
   The Storm
   Edited by Richard Hamblyn
   9780141439921

DESCARTES, RENÉ *Discourse on Method and Related*
      Writings
   Translated and edited by Desmond M. Clarke
   9780140446999

Discourse on Method and *The Meditations*
Translated by F. E. Sutcliffe
9780140442069
Meditations and Other Metaphysical Writings
Translated and edited by Desmond M. Clarke
9780140447019

The Desert Fathers: Sayings of the Early Christian Monks
Translated and edited by Benedicta Ward
9780140447316

The Dhammapada
Translated by Juan Mascaró
9780140442847

The Dhammapada
Translated by Valerie J. Roebuck
9780140449419

Díaz, Bernal *The Conquest of New Spain*
Translated by J. M. Cohen
9780140441239

Dickens, Charles *A Christmas Carol and Other Christmas Writings*
Edited by Michael Slater
9780140439052
A Tale of Two Cities
Edited by Richard Maxwell
9780141439600
American Notes
Edited by Patricia Ingham
9780140436495
Barnaby Rudge
Edited by John Bowen
9780140437287

Bleak House
Edited by Nicola Bradbury and introduced by Terry
Eagleton
9780141439723
David Copperfield
Edited by Jeremy Tambling
9780140439441
Dombey and Son
Edited by Andrew Sanders
9780140435467
Great Expectations
Edited by Charlotte Mitchell and introduced by David
Trotter
9780141439563
Hard Times
Edited by Kate Flint
9780141439679
Little Dorrit
Edited by Stephen Wall and Helen Small
9780141439969
Martin Chuzzlewit
Edited by Patricia Ingham
9780140436143
Nicholas Nickleby
Edited by Mark Ford
9780140435122
Oliver Twist
Edited by Philip Horne
9780141439747
Our Mutual Friend
Edited by Adrian Poole
9780140434972
Pictures from Italy
Edited by Kate Flint
9780140434316

Selected Journalism 1850–1870
Edited by David Pascoe
9780140435801
Selected Short Fiction
Edited by Deborah A. Thomas
9780140431032
Sketches by Boz
Edited by Dennis Walder
9780140433456
The Mystery of Edwin Drood
Edited by David Paroissien
9780140439267
The Old Curiosity Shop
Edited by Norman Page
9780140437423
The Pickwick Papers
Edited by Mark Wormald
9780140436112

DIDEROT, DENIS *Jacques the Fatalist*
Translated by Michael Henry
9780140444728
Rameau's Nephew and *D'Alembert's Dream*
Translated by Leonard Tancock
9780140441734
The Nun
Translated by Leonard Tancock
9780140443004

Domesday Book
Edited by Ann Williams and G. H. Martin
9780141439945

DONNE, JOHN *Collected Poetry*
Edited by Ilona Bell
9780141191577

Selected Poems
Edited by Ilona Bell
9780140424409
The Complete English Poems
Edited by A. J. Smith
9780140422092

DOS PASSOS, JOHN *Three Soldiers*
Edited by Townsend Luddington
9780141180274

DOSTOYEVSKY, FYODOR *Crime and Punishment*
Translated by David McDuff
9780140449136
Demons
Translated by Robert A. Maguire, edited by Ronald
Meyer and introduced by Robert L. Belknap
9780141441412
Netochka Nezvanova
Translated by Jane Kentish
9780140444551
Notes from Underground and *The Double*
Translated by Ronald Wilks and introduced by Robert
Louis Jackson
9780140455120
Poor Folk and Other Stories
Translated and edited by David McDuff
9780140445053
The Brothers Karamazov
Translated by David McDuff
9780140449242
The Gambler and Other Stories
Translated and edited by Ronald Meyer
9780140455090

The House of the Dead
  Translated by David McDuff
  9780140444568
The Idiot
  Translated by David McDuff and introduced by William
    Mills Todd III
  9780140447927
The Village of Stepanchikovo
  Translated by Ignat Avsey
  9780140446586

DOUGLASS, FREDERICK *My Bondage and My Freedom*
  Edited by John David Smith
  9780140439182
*Narrative of the Life of Frederick Douglass, an American
    Slave*
  Edited by Houston A. Baker Jnr
  9780140390124

DOYLE, SIR ARTHUR CONAN *A Study in Scarlet*
  Introduced by Iain Sinclair
  9780140439083
The Adventures of Sherlock Holmes and *The Memoirs of
    Sherlock Holmes*
  Introduced by Iain Pears
  9780140437713
The Hound of the Baskervilles
  Edited by Christopher Frayling
  9780140437867
The Sign of Four
  Introduced by Peter Ackroyd
  9780140439076

DREISER, THEODORE *The Financier*
  Introduced by Larzer Ziff
  9780143105541

DRYDEN, JOHN *Selected Poems*
    Edited by Steven N. Zwicker and David Bywaters
    9780140439144

DUMAS, ALEXANDRE *The Black Tulip*
    Translated by Robin Buss
    9780140448924
    The Count of Monte Cristo
    Translated by Robin Buss
    9780140449266
    The Man in the Iron Mask
    Translated by Joachim Neugroschel and introduced by
        Francine du Plessix Gray
    9780140439243
    The Three Musketeers
    Translated by Richard Pevear
    9780141442341
    The Women's War
    Translated by Robin Buss
    9780140449778

DURKHEIM, EMILE *On Suicide*
    Translated by Robin Buss and introduced by Richard
        Sennett
    9780140449679

D'USSEAU, ARNAUD AND PARKER, DOROTHY *The Ladies
        of the Corridor*
    Introduced by Marion Meade
    9780143105312

DVĀTRIMŚIKĀ, SIMHĀSANA *Thirty-two Tales of the Throne
        of Vikramaditya*
    Translated by A. N. D. Haksar
    9780140455175

E

Selected Essays, Poems and Other Writings
    Edited by A. S. Byatt and Nicholas Warren
    9780140431483
Silas Marner
    Edited by David Carroll
    9780141439754
The Mill on the Floss
    Edited by A. S. Byatt
    9780141439624

EMERSON, RALPH WALDO *Nature and Selected Essays*
    Edited by Larzer Ziff
    9780142437629

ENGELS, FRIEDRICH *The Condition of the Working Class in England*
    Translated by Florence Wischnewetzky, edited by Victor
    Kiernan and introduced by Tristram Hunt
    9780141191102
The Origin of the Family, Private Property and the State
    Translated by Alick West and introduced by Tristram
    Hunt
    9780141191119

ENGELS, FRIEDRICH AND MARX, KARL *The Communist Manifesto*
    Translated by Samuel Moore and edited by Gareth
    Stedman Jones
    9780140447576

English Mystery Plays
    Translated and edited by Peter Happé
    9780140430936

English Romantic Verse
    Edited by David Wright
    9780140421026

The Epic of Gilgamesh
  Translated by Andrew George
  9780140449198

The Epic of Gilgamesh
  Translated by Nancy K. Sandars
  9780140441000

EPICTETUS *Discourses and Selected Writings*
  Translated and edited by Robert Dobbin
  9780140449464
  The Art of Happiness *
  Translated by John K. Strodach and introduced by
    Daniel Klein
  9780143107217

EQUIANO, OLAUDAH *The Interesting Narrative and Other
    Writings*
  Edited by Vincent Carretta
  9780142437162

ERASMUS *Praise of Folly*
  Translated by A. H. T. Levi and Betty Radice
  9780140446081

ESCHENBACH, WOLFRAM VON *Parzival*
  Translated by A. T. Hatto
  9780140443615
  Willehalm
  Translated by Marion E. Gibbs and Sidney M. Johnson
  9780140443998

ETHERIDGE, GEORGE, CONGREVE, WILLIAM, AND
    WYCHERLEY, WILLIAM *Three Restoration Comedies*
  Edited by Gāmini Salgādo
  9780140430271

EURIPIDES *Electra and Other Plays*
> Translated by John Davie and edited by Richard Rutherford
> 9780140446685

Heracles and Other Plays
> Translated by John Davie and edited by Richard Rutherford
> 9780140447255

Medea and Other Plays
> Translated by John Davie and edited by Richard Rutherford
> 9780140449297

Medea and Other Plays
> Translated and edited by Philip Vellacott
> 9780140441291

Orestes and Other Plays
> Translated and edited by Philip Vellacott
> 9780140442595

The Bacchae and Other Plays
> Translated by John Davie and edited by Richard Rutherford
> 9780140447262

Three Plays
> Translated and edited by Philip Vellacott
> 9780140440317

EURIPIDES, SOPHOCLES, AESCHYLUS, ARISTOPHANES AND ARISTOTLE *Greek Tragedy*
> Edited by Shomit Dutta and introduced by Simon Goldhill (various translators)
> 9780141439365

EUSEBIUS *The History of the Church from Christ to Constantine*
> Translated by G. A. Williamson and edited by Andrew Louth
> 9780140445350

Eyrbyggja Saga
> Translated by Hermann Pálsson and Paul Edwards
> 9780140445305

F

FADLAN, IBN *Ibn Fadlan and the Land of Darkness*
Translated and edited by Paul Lunde and Caroline Stone
9780140455076

FANU, JOSEPH SHERIDAN LE *Uncle Silas*
Edited by Victor Sage
9780140437461

FERDOWSI, ABOLQASEM *Shahnameh*
Translated by Dick Davis and introduced by Azar Nafisi
9780143104933

FIELDING, HENRY *Joseph Andrews* and *Shamela*
Edited by Judith Hawley
9780140433869
The History of Tom Jones, A Foundling
Edited by Thomas Keymer and Alice Wakely
9780140436228

FIRBANK, RONALD *Vainglory*
Introduced by Richard Canning
9780141196336

The First Poems in English
Translated and edited by Michael Alexander
9780140433784

Five Revenge Tragedies: Kyd, Shakespeare, Marston, Chettle, Middleton
Editied by Emma Smith
9780141192277

FLAUBERT, GUSTAVE *Flaubert in Egypt*
Edited by Francis Steegmuller
9780140435825
Madame Bovary
Translated by Lydia Davis
9780143106494
Madame Bovary
Translated by Geoffrey Wall and introduced by Michèle Roberts
9780140449129
Salammbo
Translated by A. J. Krailsheimer
9780140443288
Sentimental Education
Translated by Robert Baldick and introduced by Geoffrey Wall
9780140447972
Three Tales
Translated and edited by Roger Whitehouse
9780140448009

FONTAINE, JEAN DE LA *Selected Fables*
Translated and edited by Geoffrey Grigson and James Michie
9780140455243

FONTANE, THEODOR *Effi Briest*
Translated by Helen Chambers and Hugh Rorrison
9780140447668
No Way Back *
Translated by Helen Chambers and Hugh Rorrison
9780141392158

On Tangled Paths *
Translated by Peter James Bowman
9780141392172

FORD, FORD MADOX *Parade's End*
Introduced by Julian Barnes
9780141392196
The Fifth Queen
Introduced by A. S. Byatt
9780141181301
The Good Soldier
Edited by David Bradshaw
9780141441849

FORSTER, E. M. *A Passage to India*
Edited by Oliver Stallybrass and introduced by Pankaj
Mishra
9780141441160
A Room with a View
Introduced by Malcolm Bradbury
9780141183299
Aspects of the Novel
Edited by Oliver Stallybrass and introduced by Frank
Kermode
9780141441696
Howards End
Edited by David Lodge
9780141182131
Maurice
Edited by P. N. Furbank and introduced by David
Leavitt
9780141441139
Selected Stories
Edited by David Leavitt and Mark Mitchell
9780141186191

The Longest Journey
   Edited by Elizabeth Heine and introduced by Gilbert
     Adair
   9780141441481
Where Angels Fear to Tread
   Edited by Oliver Stallybrass and introduced by Ruth
     Padel
   9780141441450

FRANCE, ANATOLE *The Gods Will Have Blood*
   Translated by Frederick Davies
   9780140443523

FRANCE, MARIE DE *The Lais of Marie de France*
   Translated by Glyn S. Burgess and Keith Busby
   9780140447590

FRANKLIN, BENJAMIN *The Autobiography and Other
     Writings*
   Edited by Kenneth Silverman
   9780142437605

FROISSART, JEAN *Chronicles*
   Translated by Geoffrey Brereton
   9780140442007

G

GALDÓS, BENITO PÉREZ *Fortunata and Jacinta*
Translated by Agnes Moncy Gullón
9780140433050

GASKELL, ELIZABETH *Cranford*
Edited by Patricia Ingham
9780141439884
Cranford and *Cousin Phillis*
Edited by Peter Keating
9780140431049
Gothic Tales
Edited by Laura Kranzler
9780140437416
Mary Barton
Edited by Macdonald Daly
9780140434644
North and South
Edited by Patricia Ingham
9780140434248
Ruth
Edited by Angus Easson
9780140434309
Sylvia's Lovers
Edited by Shirley Foster
9780140434224

The Life of Charlotte Brontë
Edited by Elisabeth Jay
9780140434934
Wives and Daughters
Edited by Pam Norris
9780140434781

GAUTIER, THÉOPHILE *Mademoiselle de Maupin*
Translated by Helen Constantine and introduced by
Patricia Dunker
9780140448139

GAY, JOHN *The Beggar's Opera*
Edited by Bryan Loughrey and T. O. Treadwell
9780140432206

GEOFFREY OF MONMOUTH *The History of the Kings of
Britain*
Translated by Lewis Thorpe
9780140441703

GERALD OF WALES *The History and Topography of Ireland*
Translated by John O'Meara
9780140444230
The Journey Through Wales and *The Description of Wales*
Translated by Lewis Thorpe
9780140443394

GIBBON, EDWARD *Memoirs of My Life*
Edited by Betty Radice
9780140432176
*The History of the Decline and Fall of the Roman Empire
(Volume I)*
Edited by David Womersley
9780140433937
*The History of the Decline and Fall of the Roman Empire
(Volume II)*
Edited by David Womersley
9780140433944

The History of the Decline and Fall of the Roman Empire (Volume III)
Edited by David Womersley
9780140433951
The History of the Decline and Fall of the Roman Empire (Abridged)
Edited by David Womersley
9780140437645

GIBBON, LEWIS GRASSIC *Sunset Song*
Edited by William K. Malcolm and introduced by Ali Smith
9780141188409

GIBBONS, STELLA *Cold Comfort Farm*
Introduced by Lynne Truss
9780141441597

GILMAN, CHARLOTTE PERKINS *The Yellow Wall-Paper, Herland* and *Selected Writings*
Edited by Denise D. Knight
9780143105855

Gisli Sursson's Saga and *The Saga of the People of Eyri*
Translated by Martin S. Regal and Judy Quinn and edited by Vésteinn Ólason
9780140447729

GISSING, GEORGE *New Grub Street*
Edited by Bernard Bergonzi
9780140430325
The Odd Women
Introduced by Elaine Showalter
9780140433791

GODWIN, WILLIAM *Caleb Williams*
Edited by Maurice Hindle
9780141441238

GOETHE, JOHANN WOLFGANG VON *Elective Affinities*
  Translated by R. J. Hollingdale
  9780140442427
Faust, Part I
  Translated by David Constantine and introduced by
    A. S. Byatt
  9780140449013
Faust, Part II
  Translated by David Constantine and introduced by
    A. S. Byatt
  9780140449020
Italian Journey
  Translated by W. H. Auden and Elizabeth Mayer
  9780140442335
Maxims and Reflections
  Translated by Elisabeth Stopp and edited by Peter
    Hutchinson
  9780140447200
Selected Poetry
  Translated and edited by David Luke
  9780140424560
The Sorrows of Young Werther
  Translated by Michael Hulse
  9780140445039

GOETHE, JOHANN WOLFGANG VON, TIECK, LUDVIG,
    FOUGUÉ, FRIEDRICH DE LA MOTTE AND
    BRENTANO, CLEMENS, *Romantic Fairy Tales*
  Translated and edited by Carol Tully
  9780140447323

GOGH, VINCENT VAN *The Letters of Vincent Van Gogh*
  Translated by Arnold Pomerans and edited by Ronald de
    Leeuw
  9780140446746

GOGOL, NIKOLAI *Dead Souls*
Translated by Robert A. Maguire
9780140448078
The Diary of a Madman, The Government Inspector and Selected Stories
Translated by Ronald Wilks and introduced by Robert A. Maguire
9780140449075

GOLDSMITH, OLIVER *The Vicar of Wakefield*
Introduced by Stephen Coote
9780140431599

GONCHAROV, IVAN ALEKSANDROVICH *Oblomov*
Translated by David Magarshack and introduced by Milton Ehre
9780140449877

GONGORA, LUIS DE *The Solitudes*
Translated by Edith Grossman and introduced by Alberto Manguel
9780143106722

GRACIÁN, BALTHASAR *The Pocket Oracle and Art of Prudence*
Translated by Jeremy Robbins
9780141442457

GRAHAME, KENNETH *Wind in the Willows*
Edited by Gillian Avery
9780143039099

GRANT, ULYSSES S. *Personal Memoirs of Ulysses S. Grant*
Introduced by James M. McPherson
9780140437010

The Greek Alexander Romance
Translated by Richard Stoneman
9780140445602

The Greek Sophists
    Translated and edited by John Dillon and Tania Gergel
    9780140436891

GREEN, ANNA KATHERINE *The Leavenworth Case*
    Introduced by Michael Sims
    9780143106128

GREGORY OF TOURS *The History of the Franks*
    Edited by Lewis Thorpe
    9780140442953

Grimm Tales
    Retold by Philip Pullman
    9780141442228

GRIMM, BROTHERS *Selected Tales*
    Translated and edited by David Luke
    9780140444018

GROSSMITH, GEORGE AND WEEDON *The Diary of a
        Nobody*
    Edited by Ed Glinert
    9780140437324

GUIBERT OF NOGENT *Monodies* and *On the Relics of
        Saints*
    Translated by Joseph McAlhany and Jay Rubenstein
    9780143106302

GURNEY, IVOR, OWEN, WILFRED AND ROSENBERG,
        ISAAC *Three Poets of the First World War*
    Edited by Jane Potter and Jon Stallworthy
    9780141182070

H

Far from the Madding Crowd
   Edited by Rosemarie Morgan and Shannon Russell
   9780141439655
Jude the Obscure
   Edited by Dennis Taylor
   9780140435382
Selected Poems
   Edited by Harry Thomas
   9780140433418
Poems of Thomas Hardy
   Edited by Claire Tomalin
   9780140424713
Tess of the D'Urbervilles
   Edited by Tim Dolin and introduced by Margaret R.
   Higonnet
   9780141439594
The Distracted Preacher and Other Tales
   Edited by Susan Hill
   9780140431247
The Fiddler of the Reels and Other Stories
   Edited by Kristin Brady and Keith Wilson
   9780140439007
The Hand of Ethelberta
   Edited by Tim Dolin
   9780140435023
The Mayor of Casterbridge
   Edited by Keith Wilson
   9780141439785
The Pursuit of the Well-beloved and *The Well-beloved*
   Edited by Patricia Ingham
   9780140435191
The Return of the Native
   Edited by Tony Slade and introduced by Penny Boumelha
   9780140435184

The Trumpet-Major
  Edited by Linda M. Shires
  9780140435405
The Withered Arm and Other Stories
  Edited by Kristin Brady
  9780140435320
The Woodlanders
  Edited by Patricia Ingham
  9780140435474
Two on a Tower
  Edited by Sally Shuttleworth
  9780140435368
Under the Greenwood Tree
  Edited by Tim Dolin
  9780140435535

HARPER, FRANCES ELLEN WATKINS *Iola Leroy*
  Edited by Henry Louis Gates and introduced by Hollis
    Robins
  9780143106043

HAŠEK, JAROSLAV *The Good Soldier Švejk*
  Translated by Cecil Parrott
  9780140449914

HAWTHORNE, NATHANIEL *The House of the Seven Gables*
  Edited by Milton R. Stern
  9780140390056
The Scarlet Letter
  Introduced by Nina Baym
  9780142437261

HAZLITT, WILLIAM *The Fight and Other Writings*
  Edited by Tom Paulin and David Chandler
  9780140436136

HEBEL, JOHANN PETER *The Treasure Chest*
Translated by John Hibberd
9780140446395

HEGEL, GEORG WILHELM FRIEDRICH *Introductory
Lectures on Aesthetics*
Translated by Bernard Bosanquet and edited by Michael
Inwood
9780140433357

HEINE, HEINRICH HARZ *Selected Verse*
Translated and edited by Peter Branscombe
9780140420982
The Harz Journey and Selected Prose
Translated and edited by Ritchie Robertson
9780140448504

HENRY, O. *Selected Stories*
Edited by Guy Davenport
9780140186888

HERBERT, GEORGE *The Complete English Poems*
Edited by John Tobin
9780140424553

HERODOTUS *The Histories*
Translated by Aubrey de Sélincourt, revised by John
Marincola
9780140449082
The Histories *
Translated by Tom Holland and introduced by Paul
Cartledge
9780713999778

HERUKA, TSANGNYÖN *The Life of Milarepa*
Translated by Andrew Quintman and introduced by
Donald S. Lopez
9780143106227

HESIOD AND THEOGNIS *Theogony, Works and Days* and
    Elegies
    Translated by Dorothea Wender
    9780140442830

HEYWOOD, THOMAS *Three Elizabethan Domestic Tragedies*
    Edited by Keith Sturgess
    9780141389813

HILDEGARD OF BINGEN *Selected Writings*
    Translated and edited by Mark Atherton
    9780140436044

Hindu Myths
    Translated and edited by Wendy Doniger
    9780140449907

HIPPOCRATES *Hippocratic Writings*
    Edited by G. E. R. Lloyd (various translators)
    9780140444513

HOBBES, THOMAS *Leviathan*
    Edited by C. B. Macpherson
    9780140431957

HOFFMANN, ERNST THEODOR AMADEUS *Tales of
    Hoffmann*
    Edited by R. J. Hollingdale (various translators)
    9780140443929
  The Life and Opinions of the Tomcat Murr
    Translated by Anthea Bell and introduced by Jeremy
      Adler
    9780140446319

HOFFMAN, ERNST THEODORE AMADEUS AND DUMAS,
    ALEXANDRE *Nutcracker and Mouse King* and *The
    Tale of the Nutcracker*
    Translated by Joachim Neugroschel and introduced by
    Jack Zipes
    9780143104834

HOGG, JAMES *The Memoirs and Confessions of a Justified Sinner*
Edited by Karl Miller
9780141441535

HÖLDERLIN, FRIEDRICH *Essays and Letters*
Translated and edited by Jeremy Adler and Charlie Louth
9780140447088
Selected Poems and Fragments
Translated and edited by Michael Hamburger
9780140424164

HOMER *The Anger of Achilles* and *The Iliad*
Translated and edited by Robert Graves
9780140455601
The Homeric Hymns
Translated by Jules Cashford and introduced by Nicholas Richardson
9780140437829
The Iliad
Translated by Robert Fagles and edited by Bernard Knox
9780140445923
The Iliad
Translated by Martin Hammond
9780140444445
The Iliad
Translated by E. V. Rieu, D. C. H. Rieu and Peter Jones
9780140447941
The Odyssey
Translated by Robert Fagles and edited by Bernard Knox
9780143039952
The Odyssey
Translated by D. C. H. Rieu and E. V. Rieu and edited by Peter Jones
9780140449112

HOPKINS, GERARD MANLEY *Poems and Prose*
Edited by W. H. Gardner
9780140420159

HORACE *The Complete Odes and Epodes*
Translated by W. G. Shepherd and introduced by Betty
Radice
9780140444223

HORACE AND PERSIUS *Satires and Epistles* and *Satires*
Translated by Niall Rudd
9780140455083

HORNUNG, E. W. *Raffles: The Amateur Cracksman*
Edited by Richard Lancelyn Green
9781856132824

HOUSMAN, A. E. *A Shropshire Lad and Other Poems*
Edited by Archie Burnett and introduced by Nick Laird
9780140424744

Hrafnkel's Saga and Other Icelandic Stories
Translated and edited by Hermann Pálsson
9780140442380

HUGO, VICTOR *Les Miserables*
Translated by Norman Denny
9780140444308
Notre-Dame de Paris
Translated by John Sturrock
9780140443530
The Wretched *
Translated by Christine Donougher and introduced by
Robert Tombs
9780141393599

HUMBOLDT, ALEXANDER VON *Personal Narrative of a Journey to the Equinoctial Regions of the New Continent*
Translated by Jason Wilson and introduced by Malcolm Nicolson
9780140445534

HUME, DAVID *A Treatise of Human Nature*
Edited by Ernest C. Mossner
9780140432442
Dialogues Concerning Natural Religion
Edited by Martin Bell
9780140445367

HUYSMANS, JORIS-KARL *Against Nature (A Rebours)*
Translated by Robert Baldick and edited by Patrick McGuinness
9780140447637
The Damned (Là-Bas)
Translated by Terry Hale
9780140447675

I

J

The Turn of the Screw
   Edited by David Bromwich
   9780141441351
The Turn of the Screw and *The Aspern Papers*
   Edited by Anthony Curtis
   9780141439907
The Wings of the Dove
   Edited by Millicent Bell
   9780141441283
Washington Square
   Edited by Martha Banta
   9780141441368
What Maisie Knew
   Edited by Christopher Ricks
   9780141441375

JAMES, M. R. *Count Magnus and Other Ghost Stories*
   Edited by S. T. Joshi
   9780143039396
The Haunted Dolls' House and Other Ghost Stories
   Edited by S. T. Joshi
   9780143039921

JAMES, WILLIAM *Pragmatism and Other Writings*
   Edited by Giles Gunn
   9780140437355
The Varieties of Religious Experience
   Edited by Martin E. Marty
   9780140390346

Japanese Nō Dramas
   Translated and edited by Royall Tyler
   9780140445398

JAY, JOHN, MADISON, JAMES AND HAMILTON,
     ALEXANDER *The Federalist Papers*
   Edited by Isaac Kramnick
   9780140444957

JEFFERIES, RICHARD *Landscape with Figures* *
  Edited by Richard Mabey
  9780141392899

JEROME, JEROME K. *Three Men in a Boat*
  Introduced by Jeremy Lewis
  9780141441214
  Three Men in a Boat and *Three Men on the Bummel*
  Introduced by Jeremy Lewis
  9780140437508

JEWETT, SARAH ORNE *The Country of the Pointed Firs and
    Other Stories*
  Edited by Alison Easton
  9780140434767

JOHNSON, SAMUEL *A Dictionary of the English Language:
    An Anthology*
  Edited by David Crystal
  9780141441573
  Selected Essays
  Edited by David Womersley
  9780140436273
  The History of Rasselas, Prince of Abissinia
  Edited by Paul Goring
  9780141439709

JOHNSON, SAMUEL AND BOSWELL, JAMES *A Journey to the
    Western Islands of Scotland* and *The Journal of a Tour
    to the Hebrides*
  Edited by Peter Levi
  9780140432213

JOINVILLE, JEAN DE AND VILLEHARDOUIN, GEOFFREY
    DE *Chronicles of the Crusades*
  Translated by Caroline Smith
  9780140449983

JONSON, BEN *The Complete Poems*
    Edited by Michael Jamieson
    9780140422771
    Volpone and Other Plays
    Edited by Michael Jamieson
    9780141441184

JOSEPHUS *The Jewish War*
    Translated by G. A. Williamson and E. Mary Smallwood
    9780140444209

JULIAN OF NORWICH *Revelations of Divine Love*
    Translated by Elizabeth Spearing and introduced by
        A. C. Spearing
    9780140446739

JUSTINIAN *The Digest of Roman Law: Theft, Rapine,
        Damage and Insult*
    Translated and edited by Colin Kolbert
    9780140443431

JUVENAL *The Sixteen Satires*
    Translated and edited by Peter Green
    9780140447040

K

The Complete Poems
Edited by John Barnard
9780140422108

KEMPE, MARGERY *The Book of Margery Kempe*
Translated by Barry Windeatt
9780140432510

KEMPIS, THOMAS À *The Imitation of Christ* *
Translated by Robert Jeffery and introduced by Max von
     Habsburg
9780141191768

KENKÔ AND CHÔMEI *Essays in Idleness* *
Translated by Meredith McKinney
9780141192109

KHAYYAM, OMAR *The Ruba'iyat of Omar Khayyam*
Translated by Peter Avery and John Heath-Stubbs
9780140443844

KHUSRAU, AMIR *In the Bazaar of Love*
Translated by Paul Losensky and Sunil Sharma
9780670082360

KIERKEGAARD, SØREN *A Literary Review*
Translated by Alastair Hannay
9780140448016
Either/Or
Translated by Alastair Hannay and edited by Victor
     Eremita
9780140445770
Fear and Trembling
Translated by Alastair Hannay
9780140444490
Papers and Journals: A Selection
Translated and edited by Alastair Hannay
9780140445893

The Sickness Unto Death
Translated by Alastair Hannay
9780140445336

KIM, RICHARD E. *The Martyred*
Introduced by Susan Choi and Heinz Insu Fenkl
9780143106401

KINGSLEY, CHARLES *The Water Babies*
Introduced by Richard D. Beards
9780143105091

KIPLING, RUDYARD *Captains Courageous*
Introduced by John Seelye
9780142437711
Just So Stories
Edited by Judith Plotz
9780141442402
Kim
Edited by Harish Trivedi
9780141442372
Plain Tales from the Hills
Edited by Kaori Nagai
9780141442396
Selected Poems
Edited by Peter Keating
9780140424317
The Jungle Books
Edited by Kaori Nagai
9780141196657
The Man Who Would Be King: Selected Stories of Rudyard Kipling
Edited by Jan Montefiore
9780141442358

KLEIST, HEINRICH VON *The Marquise of O and Other
    Stories*
    Translated and edited by David Luke and Nigel Reeves
    9780140443592

KOMNENE, ANNA *The Alexiad*
    Translated by E. R. A. Sewter and Peter Frankopan
    9780140455274

The Koran
    Translated by N. J. Dawood
    9780140449204

The Koran: With Parallel Arabic Text
    Translated by N. J. Dawood
    9780140445428

L

LACLOS, PIERRE AMBROISE FRANÇOIS CHODERLOS DE
Dangerous Liasons
Translated by Helen Constantine
9780140449570

LAFAYETTE, MADAME DE *The Princesse de Clèves*
Translated by Robin Buss
9780140445879

LAGERLÖF, SELMA *The Saga of Gösta Berling*
Translated by Paul Norlen and introduced by George C.
Schoolfield
9780143105909

LAL DED *I, Lalla: The Poems of Lal Ded*
Translated and edited by Ranjit Hoskote
9780670084470

LAMB, CHARLES *Selected Prose* *
Edited by Adam Phillips
9780141392912

LAMB, CHARLES AND MARY *Tales from Shakespeare*
Introduced by Marina Warner
9780141441627

LANGLAND, WILLIAM *Piers the Ploughman*
Translated by J. F. Goodridge
9780140440874

LAO TZU *Tao Te Ching*
  Translated by D. C. Lau
  9780140441314

LAUTRÉAMONT, LE COMTE DE *Maldoror* and *Poems*
  Translated by Paul Knight
  9780140443424

LAWRENCE, D. H. *Lady Chatterley's Lover*
  Edited by Michael Squires and introduced by Doris
    Lessing
  9780141441498
Lawrence and Italy
  Edited by Paul Eggert, Simonetta de Filippis and Mara
    Kalnins and introduced by Tim Parks
  9780141441559
Selected Poems
  Edited by James Fenton
  9780140424584
Selected Stories
  Edited by Sue Wilson and introduced by Louise Welsh
  9780141441658
Sons and Lovers
  Edited by Carl and Helen Baron and introduced by Blake
    Morrison
  9780141441443
The Fox, The Captain's Doll and *The Ladybird*
  Edited by Dieter Mehl and introduced by Helen
    Dunmore
  9780141441832
The Rainbow
  Edited by Mark Kinkead-Weekes and introduced by
    James Wood
  9780141441382

The Woman Who Rode Away, St. Mawr and *The Princess*
  Edited by Brian Finney, Christa Jansohn and Dieter Mehl
  and introduced by James Lasdun
  9780141441665
Women in Love
  Edited by David Farmer, Lindeth Vasey and John
    Worthen and introduced by Amit Chaudhuri
  9780141441542

The Laws of Manu
  Translated by Wendy Doniger with Brian K. Smith
  9780140445404

LAWSON, HENRY *The Penguin Henry Lawson Short Stories*
  Edited by John Barnes and introduced by John Kinsella
  9780143180128

LEAR, EDWARD *The Complete Nonsense and Other Verse*
  Edited by Vivien Noakes
  9780140424652

LEBLANC, MAURICE *Arsène Lupin, Gentleman-thief*
  Translated by Alexander Teixeira de Mattos and
    introduced by Michael Sims
  9780143104865

LENIN, VLADIMIR ILYICH *The State and Revolution*
  Edited by Robert Service
  9780140184358

LENNOX, CHARLOTTE *The Female Quixote*
  Edited by Amanda Gilroy and Wil Verhoeven
  9780140439878

LEOPARDI, GIACOMO *Canti*
  Translated by Jonathan Galassi
  9780141193878
Zibaldone: The Notebooks of Leopardi *
  Edited by Michael Caesar and Franco D'Intino
  9780141194400

LERMONTOV, MIKHAIL *A Hero of Our Time*
    Translated by Natasha Randall
    9780143105633

LEROUX, GASTON *The Phantom of the Opera*
    Translated by Mireille Ribière and introduced by Jann
        Matlock
    9780141191508

LEWIS, MATTHEW *The Monk*
    Edited by Christopher MacLachlan
    9780140436037

LI PO AND TU FU *Poems*
    Translated and edited by Arthur Cooper
    9780140442724

Life in Verse: Journeys Through Poetry
    Edited by Alexis Kirschbaum
    9780140424812

LINKLATER, ERIC *Poet's Pub*
    Introduced by Nancy Pearl
    9780143106661

Little Red Riding Hood and Other Classic French Fairy Tales
    Translated and edited by Jack Zipes
    9780143120230

Lives of Roman Christian Women
    Translated and edited by Carolinne White
    9780141441931

Lives of the Later Caesars
    Translated and edited by Anthony Birley
    9780140443080

LIVY *Rome and Italy*
  Translated by Betty Radice and introduced by R. M.
    Ogilvie
  9780140443882
  Rome and the Mediterranean
  Translated by Henry Bettenson and introduced by A. H.
    McDonald
  9780140443189
  The Early History of Rome
  Translated by Aubrey de Sélincourt and introduced by
    S. P. Oakley and R. M. Ogilvie
  9780140448092
  The War with Hannibal
  Translated by Aubrey de Sélincourt and edited by Betty
    Radice
  9780140441451

LOCKE, JOHN *An Essay Concerning Human Understanding*
  Edited by Roger Woolhouse
  9780140434828

LONDON, JACK *Martin Eden*
  Introduced by Andrew Sinclair
  9780140187724
  The Call of the Wild, White Fang and Other Stories
  Edited by Andrew Sinclair and introduced by James
    Dickey
  9780140186512

LONGUS *Daphnis and Chloe*
  Translated by Paul Turner
  9780140440591

LONGUS, CHARITON AND ANONYMOUS *Greek Fiction*
  Translated by Rosanna Omitowoju, John Penwill and
    Phiroze Vasunia and edited by Helen Morales
  9780140449259

LU XUN *The Real Story of Ah-Q and Other Tales of China*
Translated and edited by Julia Lovell
9780140455489

LUCAN *Civil War*
Translated by Matthew Fox and introduced by Ethan
Adams
9780143106234

LUCIAN *Chattering Courtesans and Other Sardonic Sketches*
Translated and edited by Keith Sidwell
9780140447026

LUCRETIUS *The Nature of Things*
Translated by A. E. Stallings and introduced by Richard
Jenkyns
9780140447965

LYELL, CHARLES *Principles of Geology*
Edited by James A. Secord
9780140435283

M

The Mabinogion
  Translated by Jeffrey Gantz
  9780140443226

MACAULAY, LORD THOMAS BABINGTON *The History of England*
  Edited by Hugh Trevor-Roper
  9780140431339

MACDONALD, GEORGE *The Complete Fairy Tales*
  Edited by U. C. Knoepflmacher
  9780140437379

MACHEN, ARTHUR *The White People and Other Weird Stories*
  Edited by S. T. Joshi and introduced by Guillermo del Toro
  9780143105596

MACHIAVELLI, NICCOLÒ *The Discourses*
  Translated by Brian Richardson, revised by Leslie J. Walker and edited by Bernard Crick
  9780140444285
  The Portable Machiavelli
  Translated and edited by Peter Bondanella and Mark Musa
  9780140150926

The Prince
Translated by Tim Parks
9780141442259

MADISON, JAMES, HAMILTON, ALEXANDER AND JAY,
      JOHN *The Federalist Papers*
Edited by Isaac Kramnick
9780140444957

The Māhābharata (Volume I)
Translated by Bibek Debroy
9780143100133

The Māhābharata (Volume II)
Translated by Bibek Debroy
9780143100140

The Māhābharata (Volume III)
Translated by Bibek Debroy
9780143100157

The Māhābharata (Volume IV)
Translated by Bibek Debroy
9780143100164

The Māhābharata (Volume V)
Translated by Bibek Debroy
9780143100171

The Māhābharata (Volume VI)
Translated by Bibek Debroy
9780143100188

The Māhābharata (Abridged)
Translated by John D. Smith
9780140446814

MALORY, THOMAS *Le Morte D'Arthur (Volume I)*
Edited by Janet Cowan and introduced by John Lawlor
9780140430431

Le Morte D'Arthur (Volume II)
Edited by Janet Cowan and introduced by John Lawlor
9780140430448

MANDEVILLE, BERNARD *The Fable of the Bees*
Edited by Philip Harth
9780140445411

MANDEVILLE, SIR JOHN *The Travels of Sir John Mandeville*
Translated by C. W. R. D. Moseley
9780141441436

MANSFIELD, KATHERINE *The Collected Stories of
Katherine Mansfield*
Introduced by Ali Smith
9780141441818
The Garden Party and Other Stories
Edited by Lorna Sage
9780141441801

MANZONI, ALESSANDRO *The Betrothed*
Translated by Bruce Penman
9780140442748

MARCELLINUS *The Later Roman Empire*
Translated by Walter Hamilton and introduced by
Andrew Wallace-Hadrill
9780140444063

MARLOWE, CHRISTOPHER *Complete Poems and
Translations*
Edited by Stephen Orgel
9780143104957
The Complete Plays
Edited by Robert Lindsey and Frank Romany
9780140436334

MARTIAL *The Epigrams*
  Translated by James Mitchie
  9780140443509

MARVELL, ANDREW *The Complete Poems*
  Edited by Elizabeth Story Donno and introduced by
    Jonathan Bate
  9780140424577

MARX, KARL *Capital (Volume I)*
  Translated by Ben Fowkes and introduced by Ernest
    Mandel
  9780140445688
  Capital (Volume II)
  Translated by David Fernbach and introduced by Ernest
    Mandel
  9780140445695
  Capital (Volume III)
  Translated by David Fernbach and introduced by Ernest
    Mandel
  9780140445701
  Dispatches for the New York Tribune
  Edited by James Ledbetter
  9780141441924
  Early Writings
  Translated by Gregor Benton and Rodney Livingstone
    and introduced by Lucio Colletti
  9780140445749
  Grundrisse
  Translated by Martin Nicolaus
  9780140445756
  The Portable Karl Marx
  Edited by Eugene Kamenka
  9780140150964

MARX, KARL AND ENGELS, FRIEDRICH *The Communist Manifesto*
Translated by Samuel Moore and edited by Gareth Stedman Jones
9780140447576

MASEFIELD, JOHN *Spunyarn: Sea Poetry and Prose*
Edited by Philip W. Errington
9780141191607

MASTERS, EDGAR LEE *Spoon River Anthology*
Introduced by Jerome Loving
9780143105152

MATURIN, CHARLES ROBERT *Melmoth the Wanderer*
Translated by Victor Sage
9780140447613

MAUPASSANT, GUY DE *A Parisian Affair and Other Stories*
Translated and edited by Siân Miles
9780140448122
Bel-Ami
Translated by Douglas Parmée
9780140443158
Pierre and Jean
Translated by Leonard Tancock
9780140443585

MAURIER, GEORGE DU *Trilby*
Introduced by Daniel Pick
9780140434033

MAYHEW, HENRY *London Labour and the London Poor*
Introduced by Victor Neuberg
9780140432411

Medieval English Verse
Translated and edited by Brian Stone
9780140441444

Medieval Writings on Secular Women
    Edited by Elisabeth van Houts and Patricia Skinner
    (various translators)
    9780141439914

MELVILLE, HERMAN *Billy Budd and Other Stories*
    Edited by Frederic Busch
    9780140390537
    Israel Potter: His Fifty Years of Exile
    Introduced by Robert S. Levine
    9780143105237
    Moby-Dick: or, The Whale
    Introduced by Andrew Delbanco
    9780142437247
    Omoo
    Introduced by Mary K. Bercaw Edwards
    9780143104926
    Pierre: or, The Ambiguities
    Introduced by William C. Spengemann
    9780140434842
    Redburn
    Introduced by Harold Beaver
    9780140431056
    The Confidence-Man
    Introduced by Stephen Matterson
    9780140445473

MELVILLE, HERMAN, TUCKERMAN, FREDERICK GODDARD
    AND ROBINSON, EDWARD ARLINGTON *Three
    American Poets*
    Edited by Jonathan Bean
    9780140436860

MENANDER *Plays and Fragments*
    Translated and edited by Norma Miller
    9780140445015

MENANDER, ARISTOPHANES, PLAUTUS AND
    TERRENCE *Classical Comedy*
    Translated by Norma Miller, Douglass Parker and Alan
      H. Sommerstein and edited by Erich Segal
    9780140449822

MENCIUS *Mencius*
    Translated by D. C. Lau
    9780140449716

MEREDITH, GEORGE *The Egoist*
    Introduced by George Woodcock
    9780140430349

Metaphysical Poetry
    Edited by Colin Burrow
    9780140424447

MICHELANGELO *Poems and Letters*
    Translated and edited by Anthony Mortimer
    9780140449563

MIDDLETON, THOMAS *Five Plays*
    Edited by Brian Loughrey and Neil Taylor
    9780140432190

MIDDLETON, THOMAS, TOURNEUR, CYRIL AND WEBSTER,
    JOHN *Three Revenge Tragedies*
    Edited by Gāmini Salgādo
    9780141441245

MILL, JOHN STUART *Autobiography*
    Edited by John M. Robson
    9780140433166
    On Liberty
    Edited by Getrude Himmelfarb
    9780140432077

On Liberty and the Subjection of Women
Edited by Alan Ryan
9780141441474

MILL, JOHN STUART AND BENTHAM, JEREMY
Utilitarianism and Other Essays
Edited by Alan Ryan
9780140432725

MILLER, MERLE *On Being Different*
Introduced by Charles Kaiser and Dan Savage
9780143106968

MILTON, JOHN *Paradise Lost*
Edited by John Leonard
9780140424393
Selected Poems
Edited by John Leonard
9780140424416
The Complete Poems
Edited by John Leonard
9780140433630

MO ZI *The Book of Master Mo* *
Translated by Ian Johnston
9780141392103

MOLIÈRE *The Misanthrope and Other Plays*
Translated and edited by David Coward and John Wood
9780140447309
The Miser and Other Plays
Translated and edited by David Coward and John Wood
9780140447286

MOLIÈRE, CORNEILLE, PIERRE AND RACINE, JEAN *Four French Plays: Cinna, The Misanthrope, Andromache, Phaedra* *
Translated by John Edmunds and introduced by Joseph Harris
9780141392080

MONFREID, HENRY DE *Hashish: A Smuggler's Tale*
Translated by Helen Buchanan Bell
9780141442105

MONTAGU, LADY MARY WORTLEY *Selected Letters*
Edited by Isobel Grundy
9780140434903

MONTAIGNE, MICHEL DE *An Apology for Raymond Sebond*
Edited by M. A. Screech
9780140444933
Essays
Translated and edited by J. M. Cohen
9780140178975
The Complete Essays
Translated and edited by M. A. Screech
9780140446043
The Essays: A Selection
Translated and edited by M. A. Screech
9780140446029

MONTESQUIEU, BARON *Persian Letters*
Translated and edited by C. J. Betts
9780140442816

MORE, SIR THOMAS *Utopia*
Translated by Dominic Baker-Smith
9780141442327

Utopia
Translated by Paul Turner
9780140441659

MÖRIKE, EDUARD *Mozart's Journey to Prague and a Selection of Poems*
Translated and edited by David Luke and Gilbert McKay
9780140447378

MORRIS, WILLIAM *News from Nowhere and Other Writings*
Edited by Clive Wilmer
9780140433302

MOZART, WOLFGANG AMADEUS *A Life in Letters*
Translated by Stewart Spencer and edited by Cliff Eisen
9780141441467

MULTATULI *Max Havelaar*
Translated by Roy Edwards and introduced by
R. P. Meijer
9780140445169

MUNQIDH, USAMA IBN *The Book of Contemplation: Islam and the Crusades*
Translated by Paul M. Cobb
9780140455137

MURASAKI SHIKIBU, LADY *The Diary of Lady Murasaki*
Translated by Richard Bowring
9780140435764
The Tale of Genji (Abridged)
Translated and edited by Royall Tyler
9780143039495

MUSIL, ROBERT *The Confusions of Young Törless*
Translated by Shaun Whiteside and introduced by
J. M. Coetzee
9780142180006

N

NARAYAN, R. K. *Malgudi Days*
    Introduced by Jhumpa Lahiri
    9780143039655
The Guide
    Introduced by Michael Gorra
    9780143039648
The Painter of Signs
    Introduced by Monica Ali
    9780140185492
*The Ramayana: A Shortened Modern Prose Version of the
    Indian Epic*
    Edited by Pankaj Mishra
    9780143039679

NĀRĀYANA *Hitopadeśa*
    Translated by A. N. D. Haksar
    9780140455229

NASHE, THOMAS *The Unfortunate Traveller and Other
    Works*
    Edited by J. B. Steane
    9780140430677

NAVARRE, MARGUERITE DE *The Heptameron*
    Translated by Paul Chilton
    9780140443554

NERVAL, GÉRARD DE *Selected Writings*
Translated and edited by Richard Sieburth
9780140446012

*The New Penguin Book of American Short Stories from
Washington Irving to Lydia Davis*
Edited by Kasia Boddy
9780141194424

The New Penguin Book of English Folk Songs
Edited by Julia Bishop and Steve Roud
9780141194615

NEWMAN, JOHN HENRY *Apologia Pro Vita Sua*
Edited by Ian Ker
9780140433746

The Nibelungenlied
Translated by A. T. Hatto
9780140441376

NIETZSCHE, FRIEDRICH *A Nietzsche Reader*
Translated by R. J. Hollingdale
9780140443295
Beyond Good and Evil
Translated by R. J. Hollingdale and introduced by
Michael Tanner
9780140449235
Ecce Homo
Translated by R. J. Hollingdale and introduced by
Michael Tanner
9780140445152
Human, All Too Human
Translated by Marion Faber and Stephen Lehmann and
introduced by Marion Faber
9780140446173

On the Genealogy of Morals *
　　Translated by Michael A. Scarpitti and edited by Robert
　　　C. Holub
　　9780141195377
The Birth of Tragedy
　　Translated by Shaun Whiteside and edited by Michael
　　　Tanner
　　9780140433395
The Portable Nietzsche
　　Translated and edited by Walter Kaufmann
　　9780140150629
Thus Spoke Zarathustra
　　Translated by R. J. Hollingdale
　　9780140441185
Twilight of Idols and *Anti-Christ*
　　Translated by R. J. Hollingdale and introduced by
　　　Michael Tanner
　　9780140445145

Njal's Saga
　　Translated by Robert Cook
　　9780140447699

NORTHUP, SOLOMON *Twelve Years a Slave*
　　Introduced by Ira Berlin
　　9780143106708

NOSTRADAMUS *The Prophecies*
　　Translated by Richard Sieburth and introduced by
　　　Stéphane Gerson
　　9780143106753

NOTKER THE STAMMERER AND EINHARD *Two Lives of
　　　Charlemagne*
　　Translated by David Ganz
　　9780140455052

O

OKAKURA, KAKUZO *The Book of Tea*
Introduced by Peter Benfey
9780141191843

OLIPHANT, MARGARET *Miss Marjoribanks*
Introduced by Elisabeth Jay
9780140436303

The Orkneyinga Saga: The History of the Earls of Orkney
Translated by Hermann Pálsson and Paul Edwards
9780140443837

OVID *Fasti*
Translated by A. J. Boyle and R. D. Woodward
9780140446906
Heroides
Translated by Harold Isbell
9780140423556
Metamorphoses
Translated by Arthur Golding
9780140422306
Metamorphoses
Translated by Mary M. Innes
9780140440584

Metamorphoses
  Translated by David Raeburn and introduced by Denis
    Feeney
  9780140447897
The Erotic Poems
  Translated by Peter Green
  9780140443608

OWEN, ROBERT *A New View of Society and Other Writings*
  Edited by Gregory Claeys
  9780140433487

OWEN, WILFRED, GURNEY, IVOR AND ROSENBERG,
    ISAAC *Three Poets of the First World War*
  Edited by Jane Potter and Jon Stallworthy
  9780141182070

P

PAINE, THOMAS *Common Sense*
    Edited by Isaac Kramnick
    9780140390162
    Rights of Man
    Introduced by Eric Foner
    9780140390155
    The Thomas Paine Reader
    Edited by Michael Foot and Isaac Kramnick
    9780140444964

PARKER, DOROTHY *Complete Poems*
    Introduced by Marion Meade
    9780143106081

PASCAL, BLAISE *Pensées*
    Translated by A. J. Krailsheimer
    9780140446456

PAUSANIAS *Guide to Greece (Volume I): Central Greece*
    Translated by Peter Levi
    9780140442250
    Guide to Greece (Volume II): Southern Greece
    Translated by Peter Lev
    9780140442267

The Penguin Anthology of Classical Arabic Literature
    Edited by Robert Irwin (various translators)
    9780141441887

The Penguin Book of English Verse
    Edited by Paul Keegan
    9780140424546

The Penguin Book of First World War Poetry
    Edited by George Walter
    9780141181905

The Penguin Book of First World War Stories
    Edited by Barbara Korte and Ann-Marie Einhaus
    9780141442150

The Penguin Book of French Poetry 1820–1950
    Translated and edited by William Rees
    9780140423853

The Penguin Book of Ghost Stories
    Edited by Michael Newton
    9780141442365

The Penguin Book of Hebrew Verse
    Translated and edited by T. Carmi
    9780140424676

The Penguin Book of Irish Poetry
    Edited by Patrick Crotty and introduced by Seamus
        Heaney
    9780141191645

The Penguin Book of Japanese Verse
    Translated by Geoffrey Bownas and Anthony Thwaite
    9780141190945

The Penguin Book of Modern African Poetry
    Edited by Gerald Moore and Ulli Beier
    9780140424720

The Penguin Book of Renaissance Verse 1509–1659
Edited by David Norbrook and H. R. Woudhuysen
9780140423464

The Penguin Book of Romantic Poetry
Edited by Jessica and Jonathan Wordsworth
9780140435689

The Penguin Book of Scottish Verse
Edited by Robert Crawford and Mick Imlah
9780140424669

The Penguin Book of Victorian Verse
Edited by Daniel Karlin
9780140445787

*The Penguin Book of Victorian Women in Crime: The Great
Female Detectives, Crooks, and Villainesses*
Edited by Michael Sims
9780143106210

Penguin's Poems by Heart
Edited by Laura Barber
9780141191775

Penguin's Poems for Life
Edited by Laura Barber
9780140424706

Penguin's Poems for Love
Edited by Laura Barber
9780140424805

PEPYS, SAMUEL *The Diary of Samuel Pepys: A Selection*
Edited by Robert Latham
9780141439938

PEREC, GEORGES *Species of Spaces and Other Pieces*
Translated and edited by John Sturrock
9780141442242

PERSIUS AND HORACE *Satires and Epistles* and *Satires*
Translated by Niall Rudd
9780140455083

PESSOA, FERNANDO *A Little Larger Than the Entire
    Universe: Selected Poems*
Translated and edited by Richard Zenith
9780143039556

PETRARCH *Canzoniere*
Translated by Anthony Mortimer
9780140448160

PETRARCH ET AL. *Petrarch in English*
Edited by Thomas P. Roche Jnr (various translators)
9780140434484

PETRONIUS *The Satyricon*
Translated by J. P. Sullivan and introduced by Helen
    Morales
9780140448054

PINDAR *Odes*
Translated by C. Bowra
9780140442090

PIZAN, CHRISTINE DE *The Treasure of the City of Ladies*
Edited by Sarah Lawson
9780140449501

PLATO *Early Socratic Dialogues*
Edited by Trevor J. Saunders (various translators)
9780140455038
Gorgias
Translated by Walter Hamilton and Chris Emlyn-Jones
9780140449044
Phaedrus
Translated by Christopher Rowe
9780140449747

The Rope and Other Plays
Edited by E. F. Watling
9780140441369

PLAUTUS, ARISTOPHANES, MENANDER, AND
TERRENCE *Classical Comedy*
Translated by Norma Miller, Douglass Parker and Alan
H. Sommerstein and edited by Erich Segal
9780140449822

PLINY THE ELDER *Natural History: A Selection*
Translated and edited by John F. Healy
9780140444131

PLINY THE YOUNGER *The Letters of the Younger Pliny*
Translated by Betty Radice
9780140441277

PLOTINUS *The Enneads (Abridged)*
Translated by Stephen MacKenna and edited by John
Dillon
9780140445206

PLUTARCH *Essays*
Translated by Robin Waterfield and introduced by Ian
Kidd
9780140445640
Fall of the Roman Republic
Translated by Rex Warner, revised by Robin Seager
9780140449341
On Sparta
Translated by Richard J. A. Talbert
9780140449433
Rome in Crisis
Translated by Ian Scott-Kilvert and Christopher Pelling
9780140449167

The Age of Alexander
Translated by Ian Scott-Kilvert and introduced by
    Timothy E. Duff
9780140449358
The Rise and Fall of Athens
Translated by Ian Scott-Kilvert
9780140441024
The Rise of Rome
Translated by Ian Scott-Kilvert and Jeffrey Tatum
9780140449754

POE, EDGAR ALLAN *The Fall of the House of Usher and
    Other Writings*
Edited by David Galloway
9780141439815
The Narrative of Arthur Gordon Pym of Nantucket
Edited by Richard Kopley
9780140437485
The Pit and the Pendulum
Introduced by Peter Ackroyd
9780141190624
The Portable Edgar Allan Poe
Edited by J. Gerald Kennedy
9780143039914
The Science Fiction of Edgar Allan Poe
Edited by Harold Beaver
9780140431063

The Poem of the Cid: A Bilingual Edition with Parallel Text
Translated by Rita Hamilton and Janet Perry and
    introduced by Ian Michael
9780140444469

POLO, MARCO *The Travels*
Translated by R. E. Latham
9780140440577

POLYBIUS *The Rise of the Roman Empire*
  Translated by Ian Scott-Kilvert and introduced by F. W.
      Walbank
  9780140443622
POPE, ALEXANDER *The Rape of the Lock and Other Major
      Writings*
  Edited by Leo Damrosch
  9780140423501

The Portable Beat Reader
  Edited by Anne Charters
  9780142437537

The Portable Enlightenment Reader
  Edited by Isaac Kramnick
  9780140245660

POTOCKI, JAN *The Manuscript Found in Saragossa*
  Translated by Ian Maclean
  9780140445800

PREMCHAND, MUNSHI *Playground (Rangbhoomi)*
  Translated by Manju Jain
  9780143102113

The Pre-Raphaelites: From Rossetti to Ruskin
  Edited by Dinah Roe
  9780141192406

PRÉVOST, ANTOINE-FRANÇOIS *Manon Lescaut*
  Translated by Leonard Tancock and introduced by Jean
      Sgard
  9780140445596

PRINCE, MARY *The History of Mary Prince*
  Edited by Sarah Salih
  9780140437492

PROCOPIUS *The Secret History*
    Translated by Peter Sarris and G. A. Williamson
    9780140455281

PSELLUS, MICHAEL *Fourteen Byzantine Rulers*
    Translated by E. R. A. Sewter
    9780140441697

PU SONGLING *Strange Tales from a Chinese Studio*
    Translated by John Minford
    9780140447408

PUSHKIN, ALEXANDER SERGEYEVICH *Eugene Onegin*
    Translated by Stanley Mitchell
    9780140448108
    Tales of Belkin and Other Prose Writings
    Translated and edited by Ronald Wilks and introduced
        by John Bayley
    9780140446753
    The Queen of Spades and Other Stories
    Translated and edited by Rosemary Edmonds
    9780140441192

Q

R

RABELAIS, FRANÇOIS *Gargantua and Pantagruel*
Translated by M. A. Screech
9780140445503

RACINE, JEAN *Iphigenia, Phaedra, Athaliah*
Translated by John Cairncross
9780140441222

RACINE, JEAN, CORNEILLE, PIERRE AND MOLIÈRE *Four French Plays: Cinna, The Misanthrope, Andromache, Phaedra* *
Translated by John Edmunds and introduced by Joseph Harris *
9780141392080

RADCLIFFE, ANN *The Italian*
Edited by Robert Miles
9780140437546
The Mysteries of Udolpho
Edited by Jacqueline Howard
9780140437591

REED, JOHN *Ten Days That Shook the World*
Introduced by A. J. P. Taylor
9780141442129

Renaissance Women Poets
Edited by Danielle Clark
9780140424096

RICHARDSON, SAMUEL *Clarissa: or The History of A Young Lady*
Edited by Angus Ross
9780140432152
Pamela
Edited by Peter Sabor and introduced by Margaret A. Doody
9780140431407

The Rig Veda
Translated by Wendy Doniger
9780140449891

RILKE, RAINER MARIA *Letters to a Young Poet*
Edited by Charlie Louth and introduced by Lewis Hyde
9780141192321
The Notebooks of Malte Laurids Brigge
Translated by Michael Hulse
9780141182216

RIMBAUD, ARTHUR *Selected Poems and Letters*
Translated and edited by Jeremy Harding and John Sturrock
9780140448023

RIZAL, JOSÉ *El Filibusterismo*
Translated by Harold Augenbraum
9780143106395
Noli Me Tangere (Touch Me Not)
Translated by Harold Augenbraum
9780143039693

ROCHEFOUCAULD, FRANÇOIS DUC DE LA *Maxims*
Translated by Leonard Tancock
9780140440959

Of The Social Contract and Other Political Writings
Translated by Quintin Hoare and edited by Christopher
Bertram
9780141191751
Reveries of the Solitary Walker
Translated by Peter France
9780140443639
The Confessions
Translated by J. M. Cohen
9780140440331
The Social Contract
Translated by Maurice Cranston
9780140442014

RUFUS, QUINTUS CURTIUS *The History of Alexander*
Translated by John Yardley and introduced by Waldemar
Heckel
9780140444124

RUMI, JALĀL AD-DĪN MUḤAMMAD *Selected Poems*
Translated and edited by Coleman Barks
9780140449532
Spiritual Verses
Translated by Alan Williams
9780140447910

RUSKIN, JOHN *Unto This Last and Other Writings*
Edited by Clive Wilmer
9780140432114

Russian Magic Tales from Pushkin to Platonov
Translated and edited by Robert Chandler
9780141442235

Russian Short Stories from Pushkin to Buida
Translated and edited by Robert Chandler
9780140448467

S

SACHER-MASOCH, LEOPOLD VON *Venus in Furs*
    Translated by Joachim Neugroschel and introduced by
        Larry Wolff
    9780140447811

SADE, MARQUIS DE *Philosophy in the Boudoir*
    Translated by Joachim Neugroschel and introduced by
        Francine du Plessix Gray
    9780143039013

The Saga of Grettir the Strong
    Translated by Bernard Scudder and introduced by
        Örnólfur Thorsson
    9780140447736

The Saga of King Hrolf Kraki
    Translated by Jesse L. Byock
    9780140435931

The Saga of the People of Laxardal and *Bolli Bollason's Tale*
    Translated by Keneva Kunz and edited by Bergljót S.
        Kristjánsdóttir
    9780140447750

The Saga of the Volsungs
    Translated by Jesse L. Byock
    9780140447385

Sagas of Warrior-poets
    Edited by Diana Whaley (various translators)
    9780140447712

SALLUST *Catiline's War, The Jugurthine War* and *Histories*
    Translated by A. J. Woodman
    9780140449488

SAPPHO *Stung with Love: Poems and Fragments*
    Translated and edited by Aaron Poochigian
    9780140455571

SARASHINA, LADY *As I Crossed a Bridge of Dreams:*
    Recollections of a Woman in Eleventh-century Japan
    Translated by Ivan Morris
    9780140442823

ŚARMA, VISNU *The Pañcatantra*
    Translated by Chandra Rajan
    9780140455205

SCHILLER, FRIEDRICH *Mary Stuart*
    Translated by F. J. Lamport
    9780140447118
    The Robbers and Wallenstein
    Translated by F. J. Lamport
    9780140443684

SCHOPENHAUER, ARTHUR *Essays and Aphorisms*
    Translated and edited by R. J. Hollingdale
    9780140442274

SCHREINER, OLIVE *The Story of an African Farm*
    Introduced by Dan Jacobson
    9780140431841

SCOTT, WALTER *Chronicles of the Canongate*
    Edited by Claire Lamont
    9780140439892

Guy Mannering
Edited by Peter Garside and introduced by Jane Millgate
9780140436570
Ivanhoe
Edited by Graham Tulloch
9780140436587
Kenilworth
Edited by J. H. Alexander
9780140436549
Rob Roy
9780140435542
The Bride of Lammermoor
Edited by J. H. Alexander and introduced by Kathryn
Sutherland
9780140436563
The Heart of Mid-Lothian
Edited by Tony Inglis
9780140431292
Waverley
Edited by Peter Garside and introduced by Ian Duncan
9780140436600

Scottish Folk and Fairy Tales from Burns to Buchan
Edited by Gordon Jarvie
9780141442266

SEACOLE, MARY *Wonderful Adventures of Mrs Seacole in
Many Lands*
Edited by Sarah Salih
9780140439021

Selections from the 'Carmina Burana'
Translated by David Parlett and edited by Betty Radice
9780140444407

SENECA *Dialogues and Letters*
    Translated by C. D. N. Costa
    9780140446791
Four Tragedies and *Octavia*
    Translated by E. F. Watling
    9780140441741
Letters from a Stoic
    Translated and edited by Robin Campbell
    9780140442106
Phaedra and Other Plays
    Translated and edited by R. Scott Smith
    9780140455519

Seven Viking Romances
    Translated by Herman Pálssoon and Paul Edwards
    9780140444742

SÉVIGNÉ, MADAME DE *Selected Letters*
    Translated and edited by Leonard Tancock
    9780140444056

SEWELL, ANNE *Black Beauty*
    Introduced by Jane Smiley
    9780143106470

SHACKLETON, ERNEST *South: The Endurance Expedition*
    Introduced by Fergus Fleming
    9780142437797

SHAKESPEARE, WILLIAM *A Midsummer Night's Dream*
    Edited by Stanley Wells and introduced by Helen
        Hackett
    9780141012605
All's Well That Ends Well
    Edited by Emrys Jones and introduced by René Weis
    9780141016603

Antony and Cleopatra
  Edited by Barbara Everett and introduced by Janet
  Dillon
  9780141012285
As You Like It
  Edited by H. J. Oliver and introduced by Katherine
  Duncan-Jones
  9780141012278
Coriolanus
  Edited by G. R. Hibbard and introduced by Paul Prescott
  9780141016498
Cymbeline
  Edited by John Pitcher
  9780140707427
Four Comedies
  Edited by G. R. Hibbard, M. M. Mahood, H. J. Oliver
  and Stanley Wells
  9780140434545
Four Histories
  Edited by P. H. Davison, A. R. Humphreys and Stanley
  Wells
  9780140434507
Four Tragedies
  Edited by G. K. Hunter, Kenneth Muir and T. J. B.
  Spencer
  9780140434583
Hamlet
  Edited by T. J. B. Spencer and introduced by Alan
  Sinfield
  9780141013077
Henry IV Part One
  Edited by Peter Davison and introduced by Charles
  Edelman
  9780141013664

Henry IV Part Two
  Edited by Peter Davison and introduced by Adrian Poole
  9780141016702
Henry V
  Edited by A. R. Humphreys and introduced by Michael
  Taylor
  9780141013794
Henry VI Part One
  Edited by Norman Sanders and introduced by Jane
  Kingsley-Smith
  9780141017495
Henry VI Part Two
  Edited by Norman Sanders and introduced by Michael
  Taylor
  9780141017105
Henry VI Part Three
  Edited by Norman Sanders and introduced by Gillian
  Day
  9780141018430
Henry VIII
  Edited by A. R. Humphreys and introduced by C. M. S.
  Alexander
  9780141017402
Julius Caesar
  Edited by Norman Sanders and introduced by Martin
  Wiggins
  9780141012391
King John
  Edited by R. L. Smallwood and Eugene Giddens and
  introduced by Stanley Wells
  9780141016689
King Lear
  Edited by George Hunter and introduced by Kiernan
  Ryan
  9780141012292

Shakespeare's Sonnets
Edited by John Kerrigan
9780146003738
The Comedy of Errors
Edited by Stanley Wells and introduced by Randall
Martin
9780141016672
The Merchant of Venice
Edited by W. Moelwyn Merchant and introduced by
Peter Holland
9780141013954
The Merry Wives of Windsor
Edited by G. R. Hibbard and introduced by Catherine
Richardson
9780141016474
The Sonnets and *A Lover's Complaint*
Edited by John Kerrigan
9780141021997
The Taming of the Shrew
Edited by G. R. Hibbard and introduced by Margaret
Jane Kidnie
9780141015514
The Tempest
Edited by Martin Butler
9780141016641
The Two Gentlemen of Verona
Edited by Norman Sanders and introduced by Russell
Jackson
9780141016627
The Two Noble Kinsmen
Edited by N. W. Bawcutt and introduced by Peter Swaab
9780141017266
The Winter's Tale
Edited by Ernest Schanzer and introduced by Russ
McDonald
9780141013893

Timon of Athens
Edited by G. R. Hibbard and introduced by Nicholas
Walton
9780141016610
Titus Andronicus
Edited by Sonia Massai and introduced by Jacques
Berthoud
9780141019666
Troilus and Cressida
Edited by Colin Burrow
9780141016696
Twelfth Night
Edited by M. M. Mahood and introduced by Michael
Dobson
9780141014708

SHAW, GEORGE BERNARD *Androcles and the Lion*
Edited by Dan H. Laurence
9780140450132
Back to Methuselah
Edited by Dan H. Laurence
9780140450149
Heartbreak House
Edited by Dan H. Laurence and introduced by David
Hare
9780140437874
John Bull's Other Island
Edited by Dan H. Laurence
9780140450446
Last Plays
Edited by Dan H. Laurence
9780140450422
Major Barbara
Edited by Dan H. Laurence and introduced by Margery
Morgan
9780140437904

Man and Superman
  Edited by Dan H. Laurence and introduced by Stanley
    Weintraub
  9780140437881
Misalliance and *The Fascinating Foundling*
  Edited by Dan H. Laurence
  9780140450415
Plays Extravagant
  Edited by Dan H. Laurence
  9780140450316
Plays Pleasant
  Edited by Dan H. Laurence and introduced by
    W. J. McCormack
  9780140437942
Plays Political
  Edited by Dan H. Laurence
  9780140450309
Plays Unpleasant
  Edited by Dan H. Laurence and introduced by David
    Edgar
  9780140437935
Pygmalion
  Edited by Dan H. Laurence and introduced by Nicholas
    Grene
  9780141439501
Saint Joan
  Edited by Dan H. Laurence and introduced by Imogen
    Stubbs and Joley Wood
  9780140437911
Selected Short Plays
  Edited by Dan H. Laurence
  9780140450248
The Doctor's Dilemma
  Edited by Dan H. Laurence
  9780140450279

The Shewing-up of Blanco Posnet and *Fanny's First Play*
Edited by Dan H. Laurence
9780140450255
Three Plays for Puritans
Edited by Dan H. Laurence and introduced by Michael
Billington
9780140437928

SHEIL, M. P. *The Purple Cloud*
Edited by John Sutherland
9780141196428

SHELLEY, MARY *Frankenstein*
Edited by Maurice Hindle
9780141439471

SHELLEY, MARY, WALPOLE, HORACE AND BECKFORD,
WILLIAM *Three Gothic Novels*
Introduced by Mario Praz
9780140430363

SHELLEY, MARY AND WOLLSTONECRAFT, MARY *Mary and
Maria* and *Matilda*
Edited by Janet Todd
9780140433715

SHELLEY, PERCY BYSSHE *Selected Poetry*
Edited by Isabel Quigly
9780140585049

SHEN FU *Six Records of a Floating Life*
Translated by Leonard Pratt and Chiang Su-Hui
9780140444292

SHERIDAN, RICHARD BRINSLEY *The School for Scandal
and Other Plays*
Edited by Eric S. Rump
9780140432404

SHŌNAGON, SEI *The Pillow Book*
Translated by Meredith McKinney
9780140448061

SIDNEY, SIR PHILIP *The Countess of Pembroke's Arcadia*
Edited by Maurice Evans
9780140431117

SIDNEY, SIR PHILIP ET AL. *Sidney's 'The Defence of Poesy'
and Selected Renaissance Literary Criticism*
Edited by Gavin Alexander
9780141439389

SINCLAIR, UPTON *The Jungle*
Introduced by Ronald Gottesman
9780140390315

Sir Gawain and the Green Knight
Translated by Bernard O'Donoghue
9780140424539

Sir Gawain and the Green Knight
Translated by Brian Stone and edited by J. A. Burrow
9780140422955

ŚIVADĀSA *The Five and Twenty Tales of the Genie*
Translated by Chandra Rajan
9780140455199

SLOCUM, JOSHUA *Sailing Alone Around the World*
Edited by Thomas Philbrick
9780140437362

SMITH, ADAM *The Theory of Moral Sentiments*
Edited by Ryan Patrick Hanley
9780143105923
The Wealth of Nations (Books I–III)
Edited by Andrew Skinner
9780140432084

The Wealth of Nations (Books IV–V)
Edited by Andrew Skinner
9780140436150

SMOLLETT, TOBIAS *Humphry Clinker*
Edited by Angus Ross and introduced by Jeremy Lewis
9780141441429
Roderick Random
Edited by David Blewett
9780140433326

SOLUGUB, FYODOR *The Little Demon* *
Translated by Ronald Wilks and introduced by Victor
Erofeyev
9780140186383

The Song of Roland
Translated by Glyn Burgess
9780140445329

*The Songs of the South: An Ancient Chinese Anthology of
Poems by Qu Yuan and Other Poets*
Translated and edited by David Hawkes
9780141198705

SOPHOCLES *Electra and Other Plays*
Translated and edited by David Raeburn and introduced
by Pat Easterling
9780140449785
The Theban Plays
Translated by E. F. Watling
9780140440034
The Three Theban Plays
Translated by Robert Fagles and introduced by Bernard
Knox
9780140444254

SOPHOCLES, AESCHYLUS, EURIPIDES, ARISTOPHANES AND
    ARISTOTLE *Greek Tragedy*
    Edited by Shomit Dutta and introduced by Simon
    Goldhill (various translators)
    9780141439365

SŌSEKI, NATSUME *Botchan*
    Translated by J. Cohn
    9780141391885
    Kokoro
    Translated by Meredith McKinney
    9780143106036
    Kusamakura
    Translated by Meredith McKinney
    9780143105190
    Sanshirō
    Translated by Jay Rubin and introduced by Haruki
    Murakami
    9780140455625

Speaking of Siva
    Translated and edited by A. K. Ramanujan
    9780140442700

SPENSER, EDMUND *The Faerie Queene*
    Edited by Thomas P. Roche Jnr
    9780140422078
    The Shorter Poems
    Edited by Richard A. McCabe
    9780140434453

SPINOZA, BENEDICT DE *Ethics*
    Translated by Edwin Curley and introduced by Stuart
    Hampshire
    9780140435719

STEIN, GERTRUDE *Three Lives*
>   Introduced by Ann Charters
>   9780140181845

STENDHAL *Love*
>   Translated by Gilbert and Suzanne Sale and introduced
>   by B. C. J. G. Knight and Jean Stewart
>   9780140443073
>   *The Charterhouse of Parma*
>   Translated by John Sturrock
>   9780140449662
>   *The Red and the Black*
>   Translated by Roger Gard
>   9780140447644

STERNE, LAURENCE *A Sentimental Journey*
>   Edited by Paul Goring
>   9780140437799
>   *The Life and Opinions of Tristram Shandy, Gentleman*
>   Edited by Joan and Melvyn New
>   9780141439778

STEVENSON, ROBERT LOUIS *In the South Seas*
>   Edited by Neil Rennie
>   9780140434361
>   *Kidnapped*
>   Edited by Donald McFarlan and introduced by Alasdair
>   Gray
>   9780141441795
>   *Selected Poems*
>   Edited by Angus Calder
>   9780140435481
>   *Travels with a Donkey in the Cévennes* and *The Amateur
>   Emigrant*
>   Edited by Christopher MacLachlan
>   9780141439464

Treasure Island
    Edited by John Seelye
    9780140437683
The Black Arrow
    Edited by John Sutherland
    9780141441399
The Master of Ballantrae
    Edited by Adrian Poole
    9780140434460
*The Strange Case of Dr Jekyll and Mr Hyde and Other
    Tales of Terror*
    Edited by Robert Mighall
    9780141439730

STOKER, BRAM *Dracula*
    Edited by Maurice Hindle and introduced by
        Christopher Frayling
    9780141439846
Dracula's Guest and Other Weird Tales
    Edited by Kate Hebblethwaite
    9780141441719
The Jewel of Seven Stars
    Edited by Kate Hebblethwaite
    9780141198644

STOWE, HARRIET BEECHER *Uncle Tom's Cabin*
    Edited by Ann Douglas
    9780140390032

STRASSBURG, GOTTFRIED VON *Tristan with the 'Tristran'
    of Thomas*
    Translated by A. T. Hatto
    9780140440980

STRINDBERG, AUGUST *Three Plays*
    Translated and edited by Peter Watts
    9780140440829

STURLUSON, SNORRI *King Harald's Saga*
Translated by Magnus Magnusson and Hermann Pálsson
9780140441833
The Prose Edda
Translated by Jesse Byock
9780140447552

Subhâshitâvali: An Anthology of Comic, Erotic and Other Verse
Translated and edited by A. N. D. Haksar
9780143101369

SUETONIUS *The Twelve Caesars*
Translated by Robert Graves, revised by J. B. Rives
9780140455168

SUN-TZU *The Art of War*
Translated by John Minford
9780143105756

SUSO, BAMBA AND KANUTE, BANNA *Sunjata*
Translated by Gordon Innes, edited by Lucy Durán and
Graham Furniss and introduced by Lucy Durán
9780140447361

SWIFT, JONATHAN *A Modest Proposal and Other Writings*
Edited by Carol Fabricant
9780140436426
Gulliver's Travels
Edited by Robert Demaria Jnr
9780141439495

SWINBURNE, ALGERNON CHARLES *Poems and Ballads* and
Atalanta in Calydon
Edited by Kenneth Hayes
9780140422504

SYNGE, J. M. *The Playboy of the Western World and Two
      Other Irish Plays*
   Edited by W. A. Armstrong
   9780140188783

T

Selected Poems
Translated by William Radice
9780140449884
Selected Short Stories
Translated by William Radice
9780140449839
The Home and the World
Translated by Surendranath Tagore and introduced by
Anita Desai and William Radice
9780140449860

The Táin
Translated by Ciaran Carson
9780140455304

The Tale of the Heike
Translated by Royall Tyler
9780670025138

Tales from 1,001 Nights
Translated by Malcolm C. Lyons with Ursula Lyons and
introduced by Robert Irwin
9780141191669

Tales from the Thousand and One Nights
Translated by N. J. Dawood
9780140442892

*Tales of the German Imagination from the Brothers Grimm
to Ingeborg Bachmann*
Translated and edited by Peter Wortsman
9780141198804

The Talmud: A Selection
Translated and edited by Norman Solomon
9780141441788

TENNYSON, ALFRED, LORD *Idylls of the King*
  Edited by J. M. Gray
  9780140422535
Selected Poems
  Edited by Christopher Ricks
  9780140424430

TERENCE *The Comedies*
  Translated by Betty Radice
  9780140443240

TERRENCE, ARISTOPHANES, MENANDER AND
    PLAUTUS *Classical Comedy*
  Translated by Norma Miller, Douglass Parker and Alan
    H. Sommerstein and edited by Erich Segal
  9780140449822

TERESA, SAINT *The Life of St Teresa of Avila by Herself*
  Translated by J. M. Cohen
  9780140440737

TESLA, NIKOLA *My Inventions and Other Writings*
  Edited by Samantha Hunt
  9780143106616

THACKERAY, WILLIAM MAKEPEACE *The History of Henry
    Esmond*
  Edited by John Sutherland
  9780140430493
The History of Pendennis
  Edited by Donald M. Hawes and introduced by
    J. I. Stuart
  9780140430769
Vanity Fair
  Edited by John Carey
  9780141439839

THESIGER, WILFRED *Arabian Sands*
    Introduced by Rory Stewart
    9780141442075
  The Marsh Arabs
    Introduced by Jon Lee Anderson
    9780141442082

THOMAS, EDWARD *Selected Poems and Prose* *
    Edited by David Wright
    9780141393193

THOMPSON, JOHN *The Life of John Thompson, a Fugitive
        Slave*
    Edited by William Andrews and Henry Louis Gates
    9780143106425

THOREAU, HENRY DAVID *The Portable Thoreau*
    Edited by Jeffrey S. Cramer
    9780143106500
  Walden and Civil Disobedience
    Introduced by Michael Meyer
    9780140390445

THUCYDIDES *History of the Peloponnesian War*
    Translated by Rex Warner and introduced by M. I.
        Finley
    9780140440393

The Tibetan Book of the Dead
    Translated by Gyurme Dorje, edited by Graham
        Coleman with Thupten Jinpa and introduced by Dalai
        Lama
    9780140455267

Titanic: First Accounts
    Edited by Tim Maltin
    9780143106623

The Death of Ivan Ilyich and Other Stories
Translated by Anthony Briggs, David McDuff and
Ronald Wilks
9780140449617
The Kreutzer Sonata and Other Stories
Translated and edited by David McDuff and Paul Foote
and introduced by Donna Orwin
9780140449600
War and Peace
Translated by Anthony Briggs and introduced by
Orlando Figes
9780140447934
What is Art?
Translated by Richard Pevear and Larissa Volokhonsky
9780140446425

TOURNEUR, CYRIL, MIDDLETON, THOMAS AND WEBSTER,
JOHN *Three Revenge Tragedies*
Edited by Gāmini Salgādo
9780141441245

TRELAWNY, EDWARD JOHN *Records of Shelley, Byron and
the Author* *
Edited by Rosemary Ashton
9780141392783

TROLLOPE, ANTHONY *Barchester Towers*
Edited by Robin Gilmour and introduced by John
Kenneth Galbraith
9780140432039
Can You Forgive Her?
Edited by Stephen Wall
9780140430868
Dr Thorne
Introduced by Ruth Rendell
9780140433265

Dr Wortle's School
  Edited by Mick Imlah
  9780140434040
Framley Parsonage
  Edited by David Skilton and Peter Miles
  9780140432138
He Knew He Was Right
  Edited by Frank Kermode
  9780140433913
Phineas Finn
  Edited by John Sutherland
  9780140430851
Phineas Redux
  Edited by Gregg A. Hecimovich
  9780140437621
The Duke's Children
  Edited by Dinah Birch
  9780140433449
The Eustace Diamonds
  Edited by John Sutherland and Stephen Gill
  9780141441207
The Last Chronicle of Barset
  Introduced by Sophie Gilmartin
  9780140437522
The Prime Minister
  Edited by David Skilton
  9780140433494
The Small House at Allington
  Edited by Julian Thompson
  9780140433258
The Warden
  Edited by Robin Gilmour
  9780140432145

The Way We Live Now
    Edited by Frank Kermode
    9780140433920

TROLLOPE, FANNY *Domestic Manners of the Americans*
    Edited by Pamela Neville-Sington
    9780140435610

TROYES, CHRÉTIEN DE *Arthurian Romances*
    Translated by William W. Kibler
    9780140445213

TURGENEV, IVAN *Fathers and Sons*
    Translated by Peter Carson and introduced by Rosamund
        Bartlett and Tatyana Tolstaya
    9780141441337
Fathers and Sons
    Translated by Rosemary Edmonds
    9780140441475
First Love
    Translated by Isaiah Berlin and introduced by V. S.
        Pritchett
    9780140443356
Home of the Gentry
    Translated by Richard Freeborn
    9780140442243
On the Eve
    Translated by Gilbert Gardiner
    9780140440096
Rudin
    Translated by Richard Freeborn
    9780140443042
Sketches from a Hunter's Album
    Translated by Richard Freeborn
    9780140445220

Spring Torrents
Translated by Leonard Schapiro
9780140443691

TWAIN, MARK *A Connecticut Yankee at King Arthur's Court*
Edited by Justin Kaplan
9780140430646
A Tramp Abroad
Edited by Robert Gray Bruce and Hamlin Hill
9780140436082
Autobiographical Writings
Edited by R. Kent Rasmussen
9780143106678
Life on the Mississippi
Edited and introduced by James M. Cox
9780140390506
Pudd'nhead Wilson
Edited by Malcolm Bradbury
9780140430400
Roughing It
Edited by Hamlin Hill
9780140390100
The Adventures of Huckleberry Fin
Edited by Peter Coveney
9780141439648
The Adventures of Tom Sawyer
Edited by Guy Cardwell and introduced by John Seelye
9780143039563
The Innocents Abroad
Introduced by Tom Quirk
9780142437087
The Prince and the Pauper
Introduced by Jerry Griswold
9780140436693

TYNDALE, WILLIAM *The Obedience of a Christian Man*
   Edited by David Daniell
   9780140434774

U

The Upanishads
Translated by Juan Mascaró
9780140441635

The Upanishads
Translated by Valerie J. Roebuck
9780140447491

V

VICO, GIAMBATTISTA *New Science*
    Translated by David Marsh and introduced by Anthony
      Grafton
    9780140435696

VIGNY, ALFRED DE *The Warrior's Life* *
    Translated by Roger Gard
    9780141392806

VILLEHARDOUIN, GEOFFREY DE AND JOINVILLE,
    JEAN DE *Chronicles of the Crusades*
    Translated by Caroline Smith
    9780140449983

The Vinland Sagas
    Translated by Keneva Kunz and introduced by Gísli
      Sigurðsson
    9780140447767

The Vinland Sagas
    Translated by Magnus Magnusson and Herman Pálsson
    9780140441543

VIRGIL *The Aeneid*
    Translated by John Dryden and edited by Frederick M.
      Keener
    9780140446272
  The Aeneid
    Translated by Robert Fagles and introduced by Bernard
      Knox
    9780143106296
  The Aeneid
    Translated by W. F. Jackson Knight
    9780140440515
  The Aeneid
    Translated by David West
    9780140449327

The Eclogues
Translated by Guy Lee
9780140444193
The Georgics
Translated by L. P. Wilkinson and edited by Betty Radice
9780140444148
The Georgics: A Poem of the Land
Translated by Kimberly Johnson
9780140455632

VITRUVIUS *On Architecture*
Translated by Richard Schofield and introduced by
Robert Tavernor
9780141441689

VOLTAIRE *Candide: or, Optimism*
Translated by Theo Cuffe and introduced by Michael
Wood
9780140455106
Letters on England
Translated and edited by Leonard Tancock
9780140443868
Micromegas and Other Short Fictions
Translated and edited by Theo Cuffe and introduced by
Haydn Mason
9780140446869
Philosophical Dictionary
Translated by Theodore Besterman
9780140442571
Zadig and *L'Ingénu*
Translated by John Butt
9780140441260

VORAGINE, JACOBUS DE *The Golden Legend*
Translated by Christopher Stace and introduced by
Richard Hamer
9780140446487

W

WELLS, H. G. *A Modern Utopia*
  Edited by Gregory Claeys and Patrick Parrinder and
  introduced by Francis Wheen
  9780141441122
A Short History of the World
  Edited by Michael Sherborne and introduced by Norman
  Stone
  9780141441825
Ann Veronica
  Edited by Sita Schütt and introduced by Margaret
  Drabble
  9780141441092
Kipps
  Edited by Simon J. James and introduced by David
  Lodge
  9780141441108
Love and Mr Lewisham
  Edited by Simon J. James and introduced by Gillian Beer
  9780141441054
The Country of the Blind and Other Selected Stories
  Edited by Patrick Parrinder and and introduced by Neil
  Gaiman
  9780141441986
The First Men in the Moon
  Edited by Patrick Parrinder and introduced by China
  Miéville
  9780141441085
The History of Mr Polly
  Edited by Simon J. James and introduced by John
  Sutherland
  9780141441078
The Invisible Man
  Edited by Patrick Parrinder and introduced by
  Christopher Priest
  9780141439983

The Island of Dr Moreau
   Edited by Patrick Parrinder and introduced by Margaret
   Atwood
   9780141441023
The New Machiavelli
   Edited by Simon J. James and introduced by Michael
   Foot
   9780141439990
The Shape of Things to Come
   Edited by Patrick Parrinder and introduced by John
   Clute
   9780141441047
The Sleeper Awakes
   Edited and introduced by Patrick Parrinder
   9780141441061
The Time Machine
   Edited by Patrick Parrinder and introduced by Marina
   Warner
   9780141439976
The War in the Air
   Edited by Patrick Parrinder and introduced by Jay
   Winter
   9780141441306
The War of the Worlds
   Edited by Patrick Parrinder and introduced by Brian
   Aldiss
   9780141441030
Tono-Bungay
   Edited by Patrick Parrinder and introduced by Edward
   Mendelson
   9780141441115

WHARTON, EDITH *Ethan Frome*
   Edited by Elizabeth Ammons
   9780142437803

The Age of Innocence
Introduced by Cynthia Griffin Wolff
9780140189704
The Custom of the Country
Edited by Linda Wagner-Martin
9780143039709
The House of Mirth
Edited by Cynthia Griffin Wolff
9780140187298
Three Novels of New York
Introduced by Jonathan Franzen
9780143106555

WHITE, GILBERT *The Natural History of Selborne*
Edited by Richard Mabey
9780140431124

WHITMAN, WALT *Leaves of Grass*
Edited by Malcolm Cowley
9780140421996
The Complete Poems
Edited by Francis Murphy
9780140424515

WILDE, OSCAR *De Profundis and Other Prison Writings*
Edited by Colm Tóibín
9780140439908
*Nothing ... Except My Genius: The Wit and Wisdom
of Oscar Wilde*
9780141192680
The Ballad of Reading Gaol and Other Poems
9780141192673
*The Canterville Ghost, The Happy Prince and Other
Stories*
9780141192666

The Complete Short Fiction
  Edited by Ian Small
  9780141439693
The Decay of Lying and Other Essays
  9780141192659
The Importance of Being Earnest and Other Plays
  Edited by Richard Allen Cave
  9780140436068
The Picture of Dorian Gray
  Edited by Robert Mighall and introduced by and Peter
    Ackroyd
  9780141439570
*The Soul of Man Under Socialism and Selected Critical
    Prose*
  Edited by Linda Dowling
  9780140433876

WILSON, HARRIET E. *Our Nig: or, Sketches from the Life
    of a Free Black*
  Edited by P. Gabrielle Foreman and Reginald H. Pitts
  9780143105763

WOLLSTONECRAFT, MARY *A Vindication of the Rights of
    Woman*
  Edited by Miriam Brody
  9780141441252

WOLLSTONECRAFT, MARY AND GODWIN, WILLIAM
  A Short Residence in Sweden and *Memoirs of the Author
    of 'The Rights of Woman'*
  Edited by Richard Holmes
  9780140432695

WOLLSTONECRAFT, MARY AND SHELLEY, MARY *Mary and
    Maria* and *Matilda*
  Edited by Janet Todd
  9780140433715

Women Who Did: Stories by Men and Women, 1890–1914
  Edited by Angelique Richardson
  9780141441566

WOOLF, VIRGINIA *A Room of One's Own*
  9780141183534
Between the Acts
  Edited by Stella McNichol and introduced by Gillian
    Beer
  9780141184524
Jacob's Room
  Edited by Sue Roe
  9780140185706
Mrs Dalloway
  Edited by Stella McNichol and introduced by Elaine
    Showalter
  9780141182490
Night and Day
  Edited by Julia Briggs
  9780140185683
Orlando
  Edited by Brenda Lyons and introduced by Sandra M.
    Gilbert
  9780141184272
Selected Short Stories
  Edited by Sandra Kemp
  9780141183138
The Voyage Out
  Edited by Jane Wheare
  9780140185638
The Waves
  Edited by Kate Flint
  9780141182711
The Years
  Edited by Jeri Johnson
  9780141185323

To the Lighthouse
Edited by Stella McNichol and introduced by Hermione Lee
9780141183411

WORDSWORTH, DOROTHY AND WILLIAM *Home at Grasmere*
Edited by Colette Clark
9780140431360

WORDSWORTH, WILLIAM *A Life in Letters*
Edited by Juliet Barker
9780141442136
Selected Poems
Edited by Stephen Gill
9780140424423
The Prelude
Edited by Jonathan Wordsworth
9780140433692

WORDSWORTH, WILLIAM AND COLERIDGE, SAMUEL TAYLOR *Lyrical Ballads*
Edited by Michael Schmidt
9780140424621

WORDSWORTH, WILLIAM AND DOROTHY *Home at Grasmere*
Edited by Colette Clark
9780140431360

WU CH'ÊNG-ÊN *Monkey*
Translated by Arthur Waley
9780140441116

WYATT, SIR THOMAS *The Complete Poems*
Edited by R. A. Rebholtz
9780140422276

WYATT, SIR THOMAS, ET AL. *Tottel's Miscellany: Songs and Sonnets of Henry Howard, Earl of Surrey, Sir Thomas Wyatt and Others*
Introduced by Amanda Holton and Tom MacFaul
9780141192048

WYCHERLEY, WILLIAM, CONGREVE, WILLIAM AND ETHERIDGE, GEORGE *Three Restoration Comedies*
Edited by Gāmini Salgādo
9780140430271

X

Y

Z

ZAMYATIN, YEVGENY *We*
   Translated by Clarence Brown
   9780140185850

ZOLA, ÉMILE *Au Bonheur des Dames (The Ladies Delight)*
   Translated by Robin Buss
   9780140447835
Germinal
   Translated by Roger Pearson
   9780140447422
Nana
   Translated by George Holden
   9780140442632
The Beast Within
   Translated by Roger Whitehouse
   9780140449631
The Debacle
   Translated by Leonard Tancock
   9780140442809
The Drinking Den
   Translated by Robin Buss
   9780140449549
The Earth
   Translated by Douglas Parmée
   9780140443875

ON BOOKS

Michel de Montaigne

I do not doubt that I often happen to talk of things which are treated better in the writings of master-craftsmen, and with more authenticity. What you have here is purely an assay of my natural, not at all of my acquired, abilities. Anyone who catches me out in ignorance does me no harm: I cannot vouch to other people for my reasonings: I can scarcely vouch for them to myself and am by no means satisfied by them. If anyone is looking for knowledge let him go where such fish are to be caught: there is nothing I lay claim to less. These are my own thoughts, by which I am striving to make known not matter, but me. Perhaps I shall master that matter one day; or perhaps I did do so once when Fortune managed to bring me to places where light is thrown on it. I may be a man of fairly wide reading, but I retain nothing.

So I guarantee you nothing for certain, except my making known what point I have so far reached in my knowledge of it. Do not linger over the matter but over my fashioning of it. Where my borrowings are concerned, see whether I have been able to select something which improves my theme: I get others to say what I cannot put so well myself, sometimes because of the weakness of my intellect. I do not count my borrowings: I weigh them; if I had wanted them valued for their number I would have burdened myself with twice as many. They are all, except for a very, very few, taken from names so famous and ancient that they seem to name themselves without help from me. In the case of those reasonings and original ideas which

I transplant into my own soil and confound with my own, I sometimes deliberately omit to give the author's name so as to rein in the temerity of those hasty criticisms which leap to attack writings of every kind, especially recent writings by men still alive and in our vulgar tongue which allow anyone to talk about them and which seem to convict both their conception and design of being just as vulgar. I want them to flick Plutarch's nose in mistake for mine, and to scald themselves by insulting the Seneca in me. I have to hide my weakness beneath those great reputations. I will love the man who can pluck out my feathers – I mean by the perspicacity of his judgement and by his sheer ability to distinguish the force and beauty of the topics. Myself, who am constantly unable to sort out my borrowings by my knowledge of where they came from, am quite able to measure my reach and to know that my own soil is in no wise capable of bringing forth some of the richer flowers that I find rooted there and which all the produce of my own growing could never match.

What I am obliged to answer for is for getting myself tangled up, or if there is any inanity or defect in my reasoning which I do not see or which I am incapable of seeing once it is pointed out to me. Faults can often escape our vigilance: sickness of judgement consists in not perceiving them when they are revealed to us. Knowledge and truth can lodge within us without judgement; judgement can do so without them: indeed, recognizing our ignorance is one of the surest and most beautiful witnesses to our judgement that I can find.

I have no sergeant-major to marshal my arguments other than Fortune. As my ravings present themselves, I pile them up; sometimes they all come crowding together: sometimes they drag along in single file. I want people to see my natural ordinary stride, however much it wanders off the path. I let myself go along as I find myself to be; anyway the matters treated here are not such that ignorance of them cannot be permitted nor talking of them casually or rashly. I would love very much to grasp things with a complete understanding but I cannot bring myself to pay the high cost of doing so. My design is to spend whatever life I have left gently and unlaboriously. I am not prepared to bash my brains for anything, not even for learning's sake however precious it may be. From books all I seek is to give myself pleasure by an honourable pastime: or if I do study, I seek only that branch of learning which deals with knowing myself and which teaches me how to live and die well:

> 'This is the winning-post towards which
> my sweating horse must run'
>
> Propertius

If I come across difficult passages in my reading I never bite my nails over them: after making a charge or two I let them be. If I settled down to them I would waste myself and my time, for my mind is made for the first jump. What I fail to see during my original charge I see even less when I stubborn it out.

I can do nothing without gaiety: persistence and too much intensity dazzle my judgement, making it sad and weary. My vision becomes confused and dissipated: I must tell it to withdraw and then make fresh glancing attacks, just as we are told to judge the sheen of scarlet-cloth by running our eyes over it several times, catching various glimpses of it, sudden, repeated and renewed.

If one book wearies me I take up another, applying myself to it only during those hours when I begin to be gripped with boredom at doing nothing. I do not have much to do with books by modern authors, since the Ancients seem to me to be more taut and ample; nor with books in Greek, since my judgement cannot do its job properly on the basis of a schoolboy, apprenticed understanding.

Among books affording plain delight, I judge that the *Decameron* of Boccaccio, Rabelais and the *Basia* of Johannes Secundus (if they are to be placed in this category) are worth spending time on. As for the *Amadis* and such like, they did not have enough authority to captivate me even in childhood. I will also add, boldly or rashly, that this aged heavy soul of mine can no longer be tickled by good old Ovid (let alone Ariosto): his flowing style and his invention, which once enraptured me, now hardly have the power of holding my attention.

I freely say what I think about all things – even about those which doubtless exceed my competence and which I in no wise claim to be within my jurisdiction. When I express my opinions it is so as to reveal the measure of my sight and not the measure of a thing. When I find that I have no taste for the *Axiochus* of Plato – a weak book, considering its author – my judgement does not trust itself: it is not so daft as to oppose the authority of so many other judgements, famous and ancient, which it holds as its professors and masters: rather it is happy to err with them. It blames itself, condemning itself either for stopping at the outer rind and for being unable to get right down to the bottom of things, or else for looking at the matter in some false light. My judgement is quite content merely to protect itself from confusion and unruliness: as for its weakness, it willingly acknowledges and avows it. What it thinks it should do is to give a just interpretation of such phenomena as its power of conception presents it with: but they are feeble ones and imperfect. Most of Aesop's fables have several senses and several ways of being understood. Those who treat them as myths select some aspect which squares well with the fable; yet in most cases that is only the first surface facet of them: there are other facets, more vivid, more of their essence, more inward, to which they never manage to penetrate; that is what I do.

But to get on: it has always seemed to me that in poetry Virgil, Lucretius, Catullus and Horace rank highest by far – especially Virgil in his *Georgics*, which I reckon to be the most perfect achievement in poetry; by a comparison with it one can easily see that there are passages in the *Aeneid* to which Virgil, if he had been able, would have given a touch of the comb. And in the *Aeneid* the fifth book seems to me the most perfect. I also love Lucan and like to be often in his company, not so much for his style as for his own worth and for the truth of his opinions and judgements. As for that good poet Terence – the grace and delight of the Latin tongue – I find him wonderful at vividly depicting the emotions of the soul and the modes of our behaviour; our own actions today constantly bring me back to him. However often I read him I always find some new grace and beauty in him.

Those who lived soon after Virgil's time complained that some put Lucretius on a par with him. My opinion is that such a comparison is indeed between unequals; yet I have quite a job of confirming myself in that belief when I find myself enthralled by one of Lucretius' finer passages. If they were irritated by that comparison what would they say of the animal stupidity and barbarous insensitivity of those who now compare Ariosto with him? And what would Ariosto himself say?

'O what a silly, tasteless age!'
Catullus

I reckon that the Ancients had even more reason to complain of those who put Plautus on a par with Terence (who savours much more of the nobleman) than of those who did so for Lucretius and Virgil. It does much for Terence's reputation and superiority that the Father of Roman Eloquence has him – alone in his class – often on his lips, and so too the verdict which the best judge among Roman poets gave of his fellow-poet.

It has often occurred to me that those of our contemporaries who undertake to write comedies (such as the Italians, who are quite good at it) use three or four plots from Terence or Plautus to make one of their own. In one single comedy they pile up five or six tales from Boccaccio. What makes them so burden themselves with matter is their lack of confidence in their ability to sustain themselves with their own graces: they need something solid to lean on; not having enough in themselves to captivate us they want the story to detain us. In the case of my author, Terence, it is quite the reverse: the perfections and

beauties of the fashioning of his language make us lose our
craving for his subject: everywhere it is his elegance and his
graciousness which hold us; everywhere he is so delightful –

> 'flowing exactly like a pure fountain'
> Horace

– and so he fills our souls to the brim with his graces that we
forget those of his plot.

Considerations like these encourage me to go further: I note
that the good poets of Antiquity avoided any striving to display not only such fantastic hyperboles as the Spaniards and
the Petrarchists do but even those sweeter and more restrained
acute phrases which adorn all works of poetry in the following centuries. Yet not one sound judge regrets that the Ancients
lacked them nor fails to admire the incomparable even smooth-
ness and the sustained sweetness and flourishing beauty of the
epigrams of Catullus above the sharp goads with which Martial enlivens the tails of his. The reason for this is the same as
I stated just now, and as Martial said of himself: '*Minus illi
ingenio laborandum fuit, in cujus locum materia successerat*'
[He had less need to strive after originality, its place had been
taken by his matter]. Those earlier poets achieve their effects
without getting excited and goading themselves on; they find
laughter everywhere; they do not have to go and tickle themselves! The later ones need extraneous help: the less spirit they
have, the more body they need. They get up on their horses
because they cannot stand on their own legs. It is the same
with our dancing: those men of low estate who teach it are
unable to copy the deportment and propriety of our nobility
and so try to gain favour by their daring footwork and other
strange acrobatics. And it is far easier for ladies to cut a fig-
ure in dances which require a variety of intricate bodily movements than in certain other stately dances in which they merely
have to walk with a natural step and display their native
bearing and their usual graces. Just as some excellent clowns

whom I have seen are able to give us all the delight which can
be drawn from their art while wearing their everyday clothes,
whereas to put us in a laughing mood their apprentices and
those who are less deeply learned in that art have to put flour
on their faces, dress up in funny clothes and hide behind silly
movements and grimaces.

Better than any other way this idea as I conceive it can be
understood from a comparison between the *Aeneid* and the
Orlando furioso. We can see the *Aeneid* winging aloft with a
firm and soaring flight, always pursuing its goal: the *Orlando
furioso* we see hopping and fluttering from tale to tale as from
branch to branch, never trusting its wings except to cross a
short distance, seeking to alight on every hedge lest its wind or
strength should give out,

> 'Trying out its wings on little sorties'
>   Virgil

So much, then, for the authors who delight me most on that
kind of subject.

As for my other category of books (that which mixes a little
more usefulness with the delight and from which I learn how
to control my humours and my qualities), the authors whom
I find most useful for that are Plutarch (since he has become
a Frenchman) and Seneca. They both are strikingly suited to
my humour in that knowledge that I seek from them is treated
in pieces not sewn together (and so do not require me to bind
myself to some lengthy labour, of which I am quite incapable).
Such are the *Moral Works* of Plutarch, as well as the *Epistles*
of Seneca which are the most beautiful part of his writings and
the most profitable. I do not need a great deal of preparation
to get down to them and I can drop them whenever I like, for
one part of them does not really lead to another. Those two
authors are in agreement over most useful and true opinions;
they were both fated to be born about the same period; both
to be the tutors of Roman Emperors; both came from foreign

lands and both were rich and powerful. Their teachings are
some of the cream of philosophy and are presented in a simple
and appropriate manner. Plutarch is more uniform and constant: Seneca is more diverse and comes in waves. Seneca stiff-
ens and tenses himself, toiling to arm virtue against weakness,
fear and vicious appetites; Plutarch holds to Plato's opinions,
which are gentle and well suited to public life: Seneca's opinions are Stoic and Epicurean, farther from common practice
but in my judgement more suited to the individual and firmer.
It seems that Seneca bowed somewhat to the tyranny of the
Emperors of his day, for I hold it for certain that his judgement
was under duress when he condemned the cause of those great-
souled murderers of Caesar. Plutarch is full of matter. Seneca
enflames you and stirs you: Plutarch is more satisfying and
repays you more. Plutarch leads us: Seneca drives us.

As for Cicero, the works of his which are most suitable to
my projects are those which above all deal with moral philosophy. But to tell the truth boldly (for once we have crossed the
boundaries of insolence there is no reining us in) his style of
writing seems boring to me, and so do all similar styles. For
his introductory passages, his definitions, his sub-divisions and
his etymologies eat up most of his work; what living marrow
there is in him is smothered by the tedium of his preparations.
If I spend an hour reading him (which is a lot for me) and then
recall what pith and substance I have got out of him, most of
the time I find nothing but wind, for he has not yet got to the
material which serves my purposes and to the reasoning which
actually touches on the core of what I am interested in. For me,
who am only seeking to become more wise not more learned
or more eloquent, all those marshallings of Aristotelian logic
are irrelevant; I want authors to begin with their conclusion:
I know well enough what is meant by death or voluptuous-
ness: let them not waste time dissecting them; from the outset
I am looking for good solid reasons which teach me how to
sustain their attacks. Neither grammatical subtleties nor inge-
nuity in weaving words or arguments help me in that. I want

arguments which drive home their first attack right into the
strongest point of doubt: Cicero's hover about the pot and lan-
guish. They are all right for the classroom, the pulpit or the Bar
where we are free to doze off and find ourselves a quarter of an
hour later still with time to pick up the thread of the argument.
You have to talk like that to judges whom you want to win
over whether you are right or wrong, or to schoolboys and the
common people to whom you have to say the lot and see what
strikes home. I do not want authors to strive to gain my attention by crying *Oyez* fifty times like our heralds. The Romans
in their religion used to cry *Hoc age!* [This do!], just as in our
own we cry *Sursum corda* [Lift up your hearts]; for me they are
so many wasted words. I leave home fully prepared: I need no
sauce or appetizers; I can eat my meat quite raw; and instead
of whetting my appetite with those preliminaries and preparations they deaden it for me and dull it.

Will the licence of our times excuse my audacious sacrilege in
thinking that even Plato's *Dialogues* drag slowly along stifling
his matter, and in lamenting the time spent on those long use-
less preparatory discussions by a man who had so many better
things to say? My ignorance may be a better excuse, since I can
see none of the beauty of his language.

In general I ask for books which use learning not those which
trim it up. My first two, as well as Pliny and their like, have no
Hoc age: they want to deal with people who are already on the
alert – or if they do have one it is an *Hoc age* of substance with
its own separate body.

I also like reading Cicero's *Letters to Atticus*, not only because they contain much to teach us about the history and
affairs of his time but, even more, so as to find out from
them his private humours. For as I have said elsewhere I am
uniquely curious about my authors' soul and native judgement. By what their writings display when they are paraded in
the theatre of the world we can indeed judge their talents, but
we cannot judge them as men nor their morals.

I have regretted hundreds of times that we have lost the

book which Brutus wrote about virtue: it is a beautiful thing
to learn the theory from those who thoroughly know the practice; yet seeing that the preacher and the preaching are two different things, I am just as happy to see Brutus in Plutarch as in
a book of his own. I would rather have a true account of his
chat with his private friends in his tent on the eve of a battle
than the oration which he delivered next morning to his army,
and what he did in his workroom and bedroom than what he
did in the Forum or Senate.

As for Cicero, I share in the common opinion that, erudition
apart, there was little excellence in his soul. He was a good
citizen, affable by nature as fat jolly men like him frequently
are; but it is no lie to say that his share of weakness and ambi-
tious vanity was very great. I cannot excuse him for reckoning
his poetry worth publishing; it is no great crime to write bad
verses but it was an error of judgement on his part not to have
known how unworthy they were of the glory of his name.

As for his eloquence it is beyond compare; I believe no one
will ever equal it. The younger Cicero, who resembled his
father only in name, when in command of Asia found there
were several men whom he did not know seated at his table:
among others there was Caestius at the foot of it, where people
often sneak in to enjoy the open hospitality of the great. Cicero
asked one of his men who he was and was told his name; but,
as a man whose thoughts were elsewhere and who kept forget-
ting the replies to his questions, he asked it him again two or
three times. The servant, to avoid the bother of having to go
on repeating the same thing and so as to enable Cicero to iden-
tify the man by something about him, replied, 'It is that man
called Caestius who is said not to think much of your father's
eloquence compared to his own.' Cicero, suddenly provoked by
that, ordered his men to grab hold of that wretched Caestius
and, in his presence, to give him a good flogging. A most dis-
courteous host!

Even among those who reckoned that his eloquence was, all
things considered, beyond compare, there were some who did

not omit to draw attention to some defects in it; such as his friend the great Brutus who said it was an eloquence '*fractam et elumbem*' – 'broken and dislocated'. Orators living near his own time criticized him for the persistent trouble he took to end his periods with lengthy cadences, and noted that he often used in them the words '*esse videatur*' [it would seem to be].

Personally I prefer cadences which conclude more abruptly, cut into iambics. He too can, very occasionally, mix his rhythms quite roughly: my own ears pointed this sentence out to me: '*Ego vero me minus diu senem esse mallem, quam esse senem, antequam essem.*' ['I indeed hold being old less long better than being old before I am.']

The historians play right into my court. They are pleasant and delightful; and at the same time man in general whom I seek to know appears in them more alive and more entire than in any other sort of writing, showing the true diversity of his inward qualities, both wholesale and retail, the variety of ways in which he is put together and the events which menace him.

Now the most appropriate historians for me are those who write men's lives, since they linger more over motives than events, over what comes from inside more than what happens outside. That is why, of historians of every kind, Plutarch is the man for me.

I am deeply sorry that we do not have Diogenes Laertiuses by the dozen, or that he himself did not spread himself more widely or more wisely, for I consider the lives and fortunes of the great teachers of mankind no less carefully than their ideas and doctrines.

In this genre – the study of history – we must without distinction leaf our way through all kinds of authors, ancient and modern, in pidgin and in French, so as to learn about the *matter* which they treat in their divergent ways. But Caesar seems to me to deserve special study, not only to learn historical facts but on his own account, since his perfection excels that of all others, even including Sallust.

I certainly read Caesar with rather more reverence and awe

than is usual for the works of men, at times considering the man himself through his deeds and the miracle of his greatness, at others the purity and the inimitable polish of his language which not only surpassed that of all other historians, as Cicero said, but perhaps that of Cicero himself. There is such a lack of bias in his judgement when he talks of his enemies that the only thing you can reproach him with, apart from the deceptive colours under which he seeks to hide his bad cause and the filth of his pernicious ambition, is that he talks of himself too sparingly. For so many great things cannot have been done by him without he himself contributing more to them than he includes in his books.

I like either very simple historians or else outstanding ones. The simple ones, who have nothing of their own to contribute, merely bringing to their task care and diligence in collecting everything which comes to their attention and chronicling in good faith without choice or selection, leave our judgement intact for the discerning of the truth. Among others there is for example that good man Froissart who strides with such frank sincerity through his enterprise that when he has made an error he is never afraid to admit it and to correct it at whatever point he has reached when told about it; and he relates all the various rumours which were current and the differing reports made to him. Here is the very stuff of history, naked and unshaped: each man can draw such profit from it as his understanding allows.

The truly outstanding historians are capable of choosing what is worth knowing; they can select which of two reports is the more likely; from the endowments and humours of princes they can draw conclusions about their intentions and attribute appropriate words to them. Such historians are right to assume the authority of controlling what we accept by what they do: but that certainly belongs to very few.

Those who lie in between (as most historians do) spoil everything for us: they want to chew things over for us; they give themselves the right to make judgements and consequently bend history to their own ideas: for once our judgement leans to one side we cannot stop ourselves twisting and distorting the narration to that bias. They take on the task of choosing what is worth knowing, often hiding from us some speech or private action which would have taught us much more; they leave out things they find incredible because they do not understand them, and doubtless leave out others because they do not know how to put them into good Latin or French. Let them make a display of their rhetoric and their arguments if they dare to; let them judge as they like: but let them leave us the means of making out own judgements after them; let them not deprave by their abridgements nor arrange by their selection anything of material substance, but rather let them pass it all on to us purely and wholly, in all its dimensions.

As often as not, and especially in our own times, historiographers are appointed from among quite commonplace people, simply on account of their knowing how to write well, as though we wanted to learn grammar! They are right, having been paid to do that and having nothing but chatter to sell, to worry mainly about that aspect. And so with many a fine phrase they spin a web of rumours gathered at the crossroads of our cities.

The only good histories are those written by men who were actually in charge of affairs or who played some part in that charge, or who at least were fortunate enough to have been in charge of others of a similar kind. Such were virtually all the Greek and Roman historians. For, with several eye-witnesses having written on the same subject (as happened in those days when greatness and learning were commonly found together), if an error were made it must have been wonderfully slight, or concern some incident open to great doubt.

What can we hope from a doctor who writes about war, or a schoolboy writing about the designs of kings?

To realize how scrupulous the Romans were over this, we need only one example: Asinius Pollio found even in Caesar's histories some mistakes into which he had fallen because he had not been able to look with his own eyes at every part of his army and had believed individual men who had reported to him things which were often inadequately verified, or else because he had not been carefully enough informed by his commanders-delegate of their conduct of affairs during his absence.

We can see from that example what a delicate thing our quest for truth is when we cannot even rely on the commander's knowledge of a battle he has fought nor on the soldiers' accounts of what went on round them unless, as in a judicial enquiry, we confront witnesses and accept objections to alleged proofs of the finer points of every occurrence. Truly, the knowledge we have of our own affairs is much slacker. But that has been adequately treated by Bodin, and in conformity with my own ideas.

To help my defective and treacherous memory a little – and it is so extremely bad that I have more than once happened to pick up again, thinking it new and unknown to me, a book which I had carefully read several years earlier and scribbled all over with my notes – I have for some time now adopted the practice of adding at the end of each book (I mean of each book which I intend to read only once) the date when I finished reading it and the general judgement I drew from it, in order to show me again the general idea and impression I had conceived of its author when reading it. I would like to transcribe here some of those annotations.

Here is what I put about ten years ago on my Guicciardini (for no matter what language is spoken by books, I speak to them in my own):

'He is an industrious writer of history, from whom in my judgement we can learn the truth about the affairs of his time more accurately than any other; moreover he played a part in most of them, holding an honoured position. There is no sign that he ever disguised anything through hatred, favour or vanity; that is vouched for by the unfettered judgements he makes of the great, especially of those by whom he had been promoted to serve in responsible positions, such as Pope Clement VII. As for the quality in which he seems to want most to excel, namely his digressions and reflections, some are excellent and enriched by beautiful sketches; but he enjoyed them too much: he did not want to leave anything out, yet his subject was a full and ample one – infinite almost – and so he can become sloppy and somewhat redolent of academic chatter. I have also been struck by the following: that among all his judgements on minds or actions, among so many motives and intentions, he attributes not one of them to virtue, religious scruple or conscience, as if those qualities had been entirely snuffed out in our world; and among all these deeds, no matter how beautiful they might seem in themselves, he attributes their cause to some evil opportunity or gain. It is impossible to conceive that among the innumerable actions on which he makes a judgement there were not at least some produced by means of reason. No corruption can have infected everyone so totally that there was not some man or other who escaped the contagion. That leads me to fear that his own taste was somewhat corrupted: perhaps he happened to base his estimates of others on himself.'

This is what I have on my Philippe de Commines: 'You will find the language here smooth and delightful, of a natural simplicity; the narration pure, with the good faith of the author manifestly shining through it; himself free from vanity when talking of himself, and of favour and of envy when talking of others, together with a fine zeal for truth rather than any unusual acuteness; and from end to end, authority and weight showing him to be a man of good extraction and brought up to great affairs.'

And on the *Memoirs* of Monsieur du Bellay, the following:

It is always a pleasure to see things written about by those who had assayed how to manage them, but there is no denying that in these two noblemen there is clearly revealed a great decline from that shining frankness and freedom in writing found in older authors of their rank such as the Seigneur de Joinville (the close

friend of Saint Louis), Eginhard (the Chancellor of Charlemagne)
and more recently Philippe de Commines. This is not history so
much as pleading the case of King Francis against the Emperor
Charles V. I am unwilling to believe that they altered any of the
major facts, but they make it their job to distort the judgement
of events to our advantage, often quite unreasonably, and to
pass over anything touchy in the life of their master: witness
the fall from grace of the Seigneur de Montmorency and the
Seigneur de Biron, which is simply omitted: indeed the very
name of Madame d'Estampes is not to be found in them! Secret
deeds can be hushed up, but to keep silent about things which
everyone knows about, especially things which led to public
actions of such consequence, is a defect which cannot be par-
doned. In short if you take my advice you should look elsewhere
for a full account of King Francis and the events of his time;
what can be profitable are the particulars given of the battles
and military engagements when these noblemen were present; a
few private words and deeds of a few princes of their time; and
the transactions and negotiations conducted by the Seigneur
de Langey which are chock full of things worth knowing and
uncommon reflections.